The Crystal Set Handbook

and Volume III of the Xtal Set Society Newsletter

The Crystal Set Handbook

and Volume III of the Xtal Set Society Newsletter

Philip N. Anderson

Lawrence, Kansas
The Xtal Set Society, Inc.
1994

Second printing 1996 (revised)

This handbook is dedicated to the thousands of crystal set enthusiasts who have built and experimented since Marconi's time.

Printed in Lawrence, Kansas
ISBN: 1-887736-03-4

Welcome to the Crystal Set Society

The Xtal Set Society, founded in 1991, is dedicated to once again building and experimenting with radio electronics. Our newsletters are packed full of projects and information about crystal radios, mostly dealing with design and electronics issues. Each issue contains a lead article, a "tidbits" section including hard to find information, membership correspondence, and a list of vendors or references. Our lead articles are written by members or our editor Phil Anderson. Sometimes we reprint a hard to find article from the 1920's or 30's. Members are encouraged to send projects and information into the Society and to correspond with each other. Is there really that much to write about Crystal Sets? Yes! Here are some titles from our lead articles over the last few years:

The Design of Unpowered AM Receivers
Radio Outfit in a Headset
A Crystal Set Revisited/Reconstructed
Marconi Type 107-A Tuner
Grounded Loopstick Tuner
Crystal Set Driven by a 400 ft Vertical
Two Quaker Oats Radios
Measuring Coil Capacitance
Home-Brew Curve Tracer
Ten Best Crystal Circuits

To join the Society and receive 6 bi-monthly newsletters see the information in the back of this book. Back issues of the newsletter are still available, including Volumes I through V.

-The Xtal Set Society, January 1996

ACKNOWLEDGMENTS

Ideas are never born complete but instead evolve through conversation and experimentation. This handbook is no exception. I am indebted, first of all, to several of the Xtal Set Society members - particularly Jerome Goggin, John Collins, Vince Vigus, David Hays, Larry Waggoner, Vern Killion, Larry Hall, James Hayward - whose articles and correspondence added to whatever strengths chapters one through three possess. I owe special thanks to Rebecca Hewes, my daughter, for creating the wonderful circuit drawings, in the style harkening back to Elmer Bucher's time (1917), and for editing and typesetting the manuscript. The handbook benefited also from the readings and comments of Randy Hewes, my son-in-law, and Pat Anderson, my wife. In particular, I owe the seed of interest to Kenneth E. Anderson, my father, who built crystal sets as a kid in the twenties in Minneapolis, Minnesota.

Philip N. Anderson

Lawrence, Kansas
May 1994

CONTENTS

PREFACE

This book is written for crystal set enthusiasts, first-time radio experimenters, electronics students, and radio amateurs. I wrote it to encourage design, building, and experimentation. For too long now, we've become appliance operators; that is, we purchase and use electronic gear but we don't dig inside it. Our future depends upon regaining the ability to create, to understand, and to build.

Crystal set builders are half way there; at least we are building. I'd like to see us reach that next step, designing and experimenting. For first-time radio experimenters, there is no better place to start in radio electronics than with the crystal set. When we grasp the rules-of-thumb and concepts that the crystal set can teach, we obtain a good foundation for further study and experimentation in modern radio electronics.

The scope of this handbook is wide. Students and hobbyists should find the introduction and most of chapters one through three easy to follow. A few articles have been written by long-time experimenters, so they may be a challenge. Comprehending the remaining chapters, not a part of the newsletters, requires a basic knowledge of DC and AC circuits and algebra. General knowledge about radio is also helpful.

In the introduction, the simplest crystal set is presented; its parts and drawing symbols are identified; and its operation is outlined. A set of plans is included, allowing the beginner to experience, firsthand, the simplicity and wonder of crystal radio. I encourage you to build this set. Reading about and then building the set clarifies the basic ideas in a way nothing else can! No special parts are required except a high impedance earplug which can be purchased by mail or at an electronics parts store.

Chapters one through three are volume III of The Xtal Set Society Newsletter. The membership correspondence and lead articles will widen your knowledge of crystal sets, and I hope will pique your interest. Some of the articles are historical while others are technical. However, the newsletter and remaining chapters do not delve into 'antique radio' subjects. The lead articles are "Who Invented Crystal Radio," "The Simplest Crystal Set," "A Simple Short-wave Crystal Set," "Did Insects Beat Us to Radio," and "The Tikker Detector Revisited." In the newsletter, members share ideas, projects, and references: a self-powered radio, an HF crystal set, a push-pull crystal set, oscillating detectors, and neat old-time books like *Practical Wireless Telegraphy* by Elmer Bucher (1917).

The remaining chapters are aimed at the builder, the experimenter, and the student. Coil formulas, coil Q estimation, coil capacitance estimation, and a wire table are presented to aid the designer and experimenter with projects. Calculation examples are included to clarify formula use. A resistor model for the AM detector is included too, which enables experiments to calculate detector and headphone loading effects without guessing.

The last chapter covers radio circuit matching. Matching is an important concept not only for crystal sets but for radio circuits in general. By examining the crystal set, we reveal the principles upon which matching is based, the maximum power transfer rule and the series-parallel equivalent circuit secret. With proper matching, a crystal set will deliver the largest volume possible for the signal received.

The crystal set embodies many of the basic concepts upon which modern radio electronics is based. By grasping these basics in their rarest form, the crystal set, you can build a powerful foundation for additional learning, for designing equipment, or simply for the joy of it.

INTRODUCTION

THE CRYSTAL SET!

The crystal set is an historic resource! This is evident given the many articles listed in the bibliography. Since Marconi's time, thousands of home-brew sets of endless variation have been built. Interest in the twenties through the forties was intense; nearly every household or farm had a crystal set builder. This enthusiasm is matched today, perhaps, only by the frenzy of home computer enthusiasts. The crystal set is the basis for modern day radio and communications equipment; the basics it embodies live on in a wide variety of radio systems. For this reason, a study of crystal sets is a great place to start to build a foundation in radio electronics.

If this handbook is your introduction to the crystal set, I urge you to build the simplest of sets from the plans outlined below. Building and experimenting complements reading; there is no better way to grasp and retain concepts. Experimentation will speak volumes to you and give you a deep and clear understanding of the roots of radio. Later on, if you build the short wave (high frequency) AM set presented, you'll also experience firsthand the constantly varying state of the ionosphere. The signals from distant stations will ebb and flow, particularly at night. Today's radios hide these minute-by-minute fluctuations that are due to the sun's activity.

If you've built or read about crystal sets before, then just dig in and have fun. If, by chance, you're not challenged by the material in the newsletters, explore the chapters on coil inductance, Q, and capacitance or the chapters on circuit matching. Watch out! These chapters are meaty. They contain the secrets of radio reception and I hope you'll have fun digging them out! Crystal set optimization depends upon these secrets: coil parameters, detector characteristics, and the principles of maximum power transfer and series-parallel equivalent circuits.

My interest in the crystal set is its simplicity and complexity; it contains few parts but exhibits many concepts. Crystal sets are a great tool for teaching and a superb hobby. If you can fully understand the basic principles, as demonstrated by the set, you will form a very good foundation for further study in radio electronics. It's not necessary that you delve into complex equations or enroll in several engineering courses to begin your journey. Formal study can come later. You can obtain an intuitive feel for radio by thoroughly examining the crystal set. So, let's start our adventure; let's examine the simplest of all crystal sets.

the simplest crystal set

The simplest set is shown in schematic form in Figure 1. It consists of just four parts: an antenna, an antenna coil, a detector, and a pair of headphones. It's been built, perhaps, a million times, on farms, in attics, in living rooms, and in fox holes over the years. Builders used this set to listen to early broadcasts such as The Shadow, the Dempsey fight, or Armed Forces News!

The antenna (A) is simply a long piece of wire. For stations broadcasting in the 550-1500 Kilohertz (Khz) band, the AM band on your pocket radio, 75 feet or so works quite well. This long wire antenna, often called an end-fed, is attached to the set and to a tree, pole, or wherever at its other end.

The antenna coil (L1) is added to resonate the antenna and, for more complex sets, to match the antenna to the detector and headphones. The coil can be wound on a cylindrical form, a match box, a Quaker Oats box, or even take the shape of a spider web. Cotton covered wire was used for sets built in the twenties; we use enameled or plastic coated wire today.

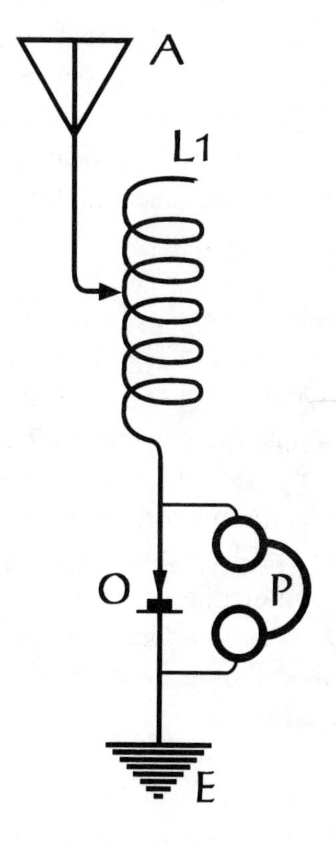

Figure 1: The Simplest Radio Receiver

The remaining parts, the detector (O) and headphones (P), work together to recover audio from the radio signal. The radio signal is converted to audio by the detector, called a diode today, and audio is heard in the headphones. This process is called rectification, basic to all radio receivers, and is discussed later.

parts and their drawing symbols

Before launching into a more detailed discussion about crystal set operation, let's examine, briefly, the various drawing symbols that are used for the electrical parts. Most of the symbols are presented in Figure 2. By connecting them together, like drawing a dot-to-dot picture, you can create circuit plans. A plan is simply a wiring schematic, showing the parts and the wires interconnecting them. Figure 1 is an example of a crystal schematic.

The drawing symbols are often based on the shape or the action of the part they represent. The antenna is no exception. Antennas built by radio pioneers consisted, often, of sets of parallel wires, tied together at a common point (a). The symbol used today is simplified (b). Coils are made by winding wire on a form, typically cylindrical, so the symbol is a spiral (c). Capacitors are made by stacking metal plates, with air or some other non-conducting material between the plates; hence, they are drawn as two lines one above the other (d). An arrow at the end of a plate denoted that the part, once wired into a set, can be adjusted.

The detector symbol (e) is also derived from its physical origin, a sharpened or thin wire pressed lightly against a hunk of galena crystal mounted in a holder. A drawing of an early galena detector is shown in Figure 3. The symbol for the modern day detector (f), the diode, is similar but simplified; its origin is not as clearly displayed. So much for modern brevity!

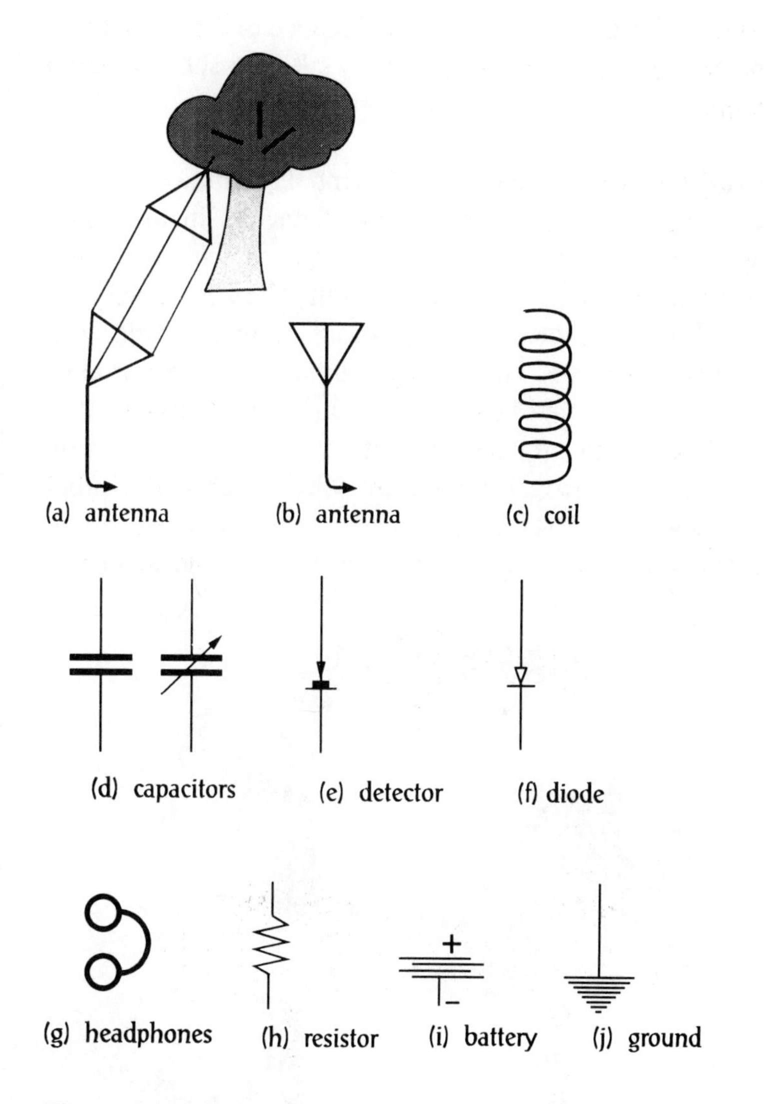

Figure 2: Parts Symbols

The headphone symbol (g) includes two circles which represent phones, one for each ear. The loop denotes the band that goes over your head and holds the phones together. The lines also indicate that the phones are wired in series.

Crystal set headphones have an impedance of 2,000 to 4,000 ohms and are not equivalent to today's 8 ohm sets for stereo systems.

The resistor, battery, and ground symbols round out our set of drawing symbols - our cast of characters in this radio show. Resistors were originally constructed with wire, and were often wound on a cylindrical form. The zigzag shape of the symbol (h) denotes the loops of added wire, resulting in additional resistance. The battery symbol (i) is a pictorial of alternating metal plates (which are, our course, suspended in acid). Take a cap off your car battery and peer inside; you will 'see' this symbol. I don't know why the ground symbol (j) is drawn as it is. Use your imagination. Perhaps a clump of grass or an upside-down antenna symbol would be just as good.

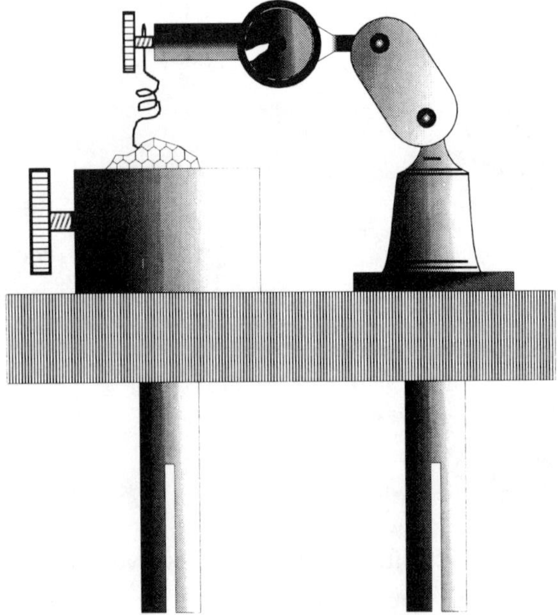

Figure 3: The galena and cat whisker detector

Using these symbols, we can draw a representation of any of the crystal sets. The result is a schematic which shows the parts used and how they are wired together. Figure 4 is a schematic of the basic conductively coupled crystal set. Let's examine how this basic set works.

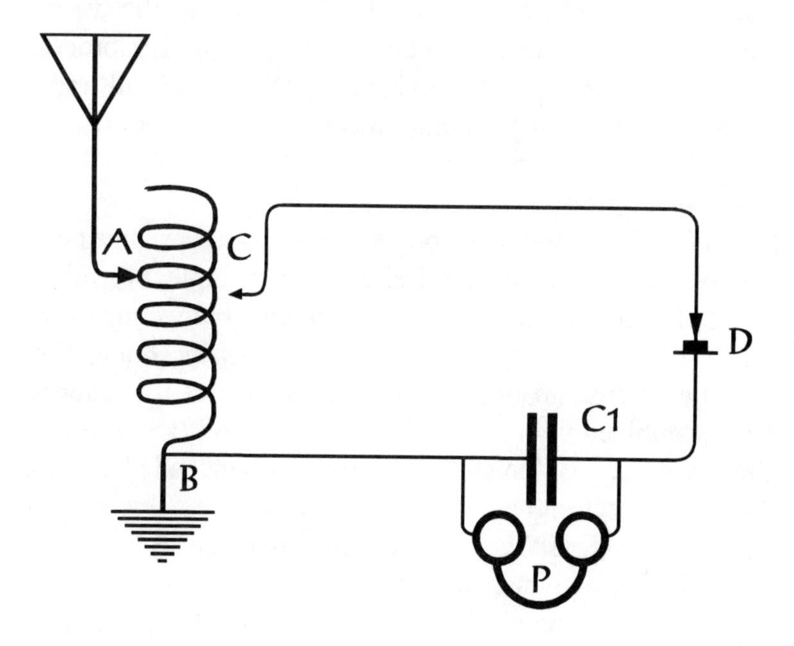

Figure 4: The Conductively Coupled Receiver

basic crystal set operation

The conductively coupled set has been popular through the years. Its popularity is derived from the fact that it is easy to build, easy to tune, and develops more volume than the basic set of Figure 1, even under less than ideal conditions. This set differs from the basic set in that the detector is wired to the top of the antenna coil or near it instead of at its bottom. It's called the conductively coupled receiver because the detector is wired directly to the coil, unlike many sets we'll investigate that add a capacitor in series with the detector.

The job of the antenna is to convert incoming radio waves into radio frequency current. The electromagnetic waves surround the antenna and induce a current in it. The process is called electromagnetic induction. Of course, all radio waves in the vicinity of the antenna produce currents, so we've added the antenna coil.

The job of the antenna coil is to help restrict unwanted signals and to boost those desired. For example, we might wish to listen to a station at 1000 Kilohertz, but we may hear one at 1300 Kilohertz also. The coil works in conjunction with the antenna to do this; the capacitance of the antenna (C) is combined with the inductance of the coil (L) to form a filter. This series tuned L-C circuit - often called a tank circuit - reduces signals it is not tuned to and retains signals it is tuned to. In effect, the crystal set is tuned by selecting the right coil to match the antenna. These basic sets do a pretty good job; however, they have a limited capability to eliminate the reception of strong stations that are on a frequency near the one we wish to isolate.

The radio frequency (RF) current, produced by the antenna and the coil, is shown graphically in Figure 5. This current will swing alternately positive and negative every radio frequency cycle. For example, if you are listening to an AM station at 1,000 Kilohertz (one megahertz), the current in the antenna will reverse direction one million times each second.

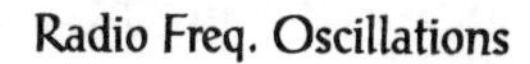

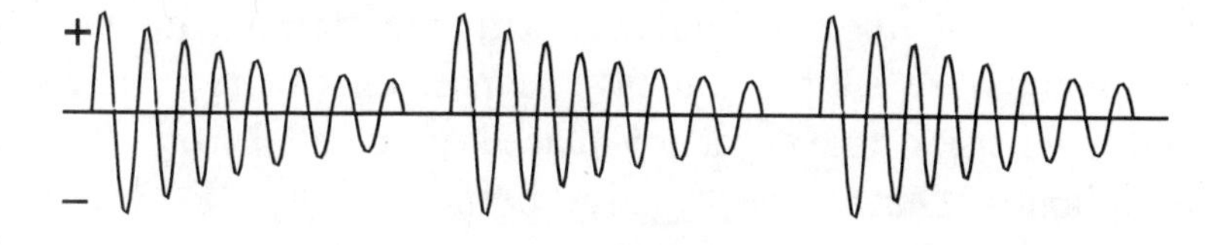

Rectified Current

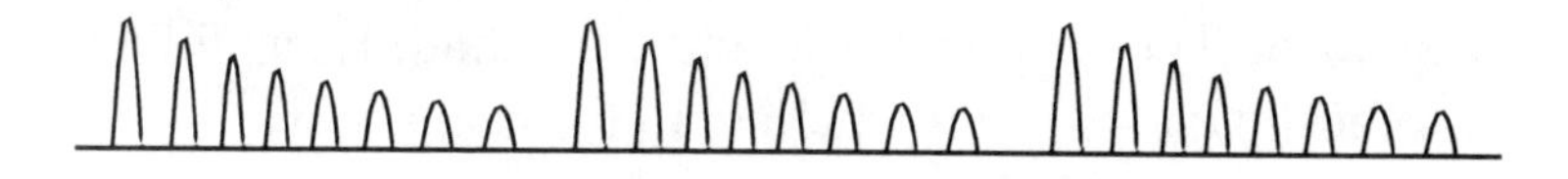

Telephone Current

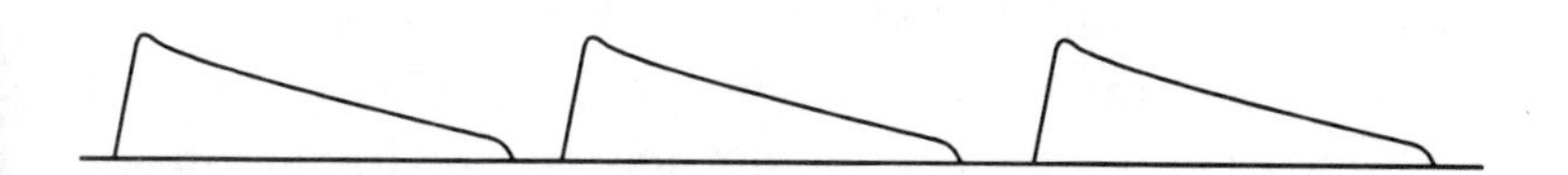

Figure 5: Radio and audio current frequency

The job of the detector is to eliminate either the positive going or negative going portion of this current, and this process is called rectification. For our set in Figure 4, the detector will conduct current when the radio frequency current is positive but not when it is negative. This is the nature of the detector. Hence, only the positive portion of the RF current, labeled rectified current in the figure, flows through the diode to the capacitor and headphones. The job of the headphones is to convert this rectified RF current into an audible tone.

How do the detector and headphones, working together, accomplish this? Think of it this way. Each time the radio signal goes positive, current will flow in the detector. But since the current is pulsating at a radio frequency, the diaphragm in the headphones will not follow it; the fluctuations are simply too fast. Hence, all of the current simply charges the capacitor placed in parallel with the headphones. During the negative portion of the RF cycle, when the diode is off (back biased), the charge on the capacitor leaks off slowly through the headphones. This is denoted by the slow slope in the telephone current, as shown in Figure 5. The diaphragm in the headphones can follow this audio-rate signal so it's audible in the headphones.

So what has happened? Let's summarize! The strength of the voltage developed on the capacitor across the headphones follows the amplitude (or peak value) of the RF antenna current. The current developed in the headphones, in turn, is proportional to the capacitor's voltage. Hence, what you hear is the changing amplitude of the RF signal. Radio signals that convey information by varying their amplitude are called amplitude modulated waves (AM)!

That's really the essence of the crystal radio set. It's job is to transfer efficiently the radio frequency energy delivered to its antenna to the set headphones. The set acts as a converter of radio signals into audio signals; that is, it acts as a radio frequency filter and a rectifier.

but what about the strength of the radio signal?

At this point you might say, "But how is this possible? The radio waves simply can't be that strong." Or you might say, "Can the ear really hear signals that weak? We don't have an audio amplifier!" The radio signal is strong enough, and your ear can hear signals that weak!

That's the beauty and the attraction of many hobbyists to the crystal set. It converts the energy of the AM broadcast signal into audio sufficient to hear without adding a battery or audio amplification! In fact, your ear is sensitive enough to detect signals that are less than a millionth of a millionth of a watt. You can hear audio tones at a lower level than radio receivers can hear radio frequency signals!

Does this mean we can listen to any radio signals we want to with a crystal set? Theoretically? Yes! Practically? No! The trick is to make sets efficient enough to process the weaker signals. Here reality sets in, and its not so easy. We can make decent AM sets for the 550-1500 Khz AM broadcasting band - your regular AM dial - but it's fairly difficult to built high frequency sets and have much success. It's also possible, barely, to make slope-detecting FM sets, but you've got to live near an FM tower! These are the challenges for the crystal set experimenter. Experimenters tell their stories in chapters one through three, Volume Three of the Xtal Set Society Newsletter. The remaining chapters develop additional theory and equations so that we can attempt to meet these challenges and dream of even more!

your first basic set

You may wish to build the basic AM broadcast band set described next before examining the newsletters and the chapters on coils, matching, and detector loading. I highly recommend that you do so if you've never built a set before. I've included a brief set of plans, a listing of assembly steps, and a drawing for building the set drawn in Figure 4. It's one of the easiest sets to build and it works well if you have a strong, local AM station.

What tools and what parts will you need? You'll want a small soldering iron, wire cutters, a pair of small pliers, and a knife or exacto-blade. The parts required are listed below.

Bill-of-materials for a basic AM Broadcast Crystal Set:

1) 75 feet of Radio Shack antenna wire, or similar
2) 100 feet of plastic coated hookup wire, say #24
3) one empty Quaker Oats box, (dump the contents in a plastic jar!)
4) one germanium diode (1N34 or similar)
5) one .001 microfarad (µfd) capacitor, any voltage spec
6) one 47,000 ohm resistor
7) one crystal set earplug (earphone), or one 2,000 ohm pair of old-style headphones
8) and some solder (and time!)

You can wire the set completely on the oat box as shown in Figure 6. Follow the steps below and check them off as you go if you like.

You'll start by winding 52 feet of hookup wire around the outside of the box.

step 1 _____. Start by punching a hole for the wire one inch from the top of the box, anywhere on the side. Thread a foot or so of wire, off the spool, into the hole from the outside.

step 2 _____. Wind forty turns onto the box. I wind the turns onto the box by holding it between my knees and then winding the wire off the spool around the box. Make sure the turns stay snug, side by side. Every five turns, twist an eyelet in the wire - but don't cut the wire - as shown in Figure 6.

Then continue winding. It may help to add masking tape as you go to hold the wire in place.

step 3 _____. At forty turns, cut off two feet of wire or so, poke another hole in the oat box right where the coil has ended, and thread the remaining wire through the hole to the inside. Keep the coil wire taught, and use tape again if need be to hold it in place.

step 4 _____. Punch another hole near the bottom of the box and thread the remaining wire out again. Trim the remaining wire to a foot or so. This will be your 'ground' terminal. Now you'll solder together the diode, resistor, and earplug. These will form the 'detector assembly.'

step 5a _____. Make the detector assembly. I am assuming that you'll use the earplug since 2,000 ohm headphones are hard to find. So move on to step 5b. However, if you do find or have a old set of headphones, go ahead and use them. In this case, wire the detector assembly as shown in Figure 6 below and move to step 6.

step 5b ____. Start the alternate detector assembly, shown at the bottom of Figure 6. If the earplug you purchased (or will buy) came with a mini-plug attached, just cut if off and then strip and tin the wire leads. By tinning, we mean apply a bit of solder to the bare wires. This will make soldering to these leads easier in the following steps.

step 5c ____. Solder the 47,000 ohm resistor across the leads of the earplug.

step 5d ____. Solder a 1N34 diode (or equivalent) in series with one of the leads of the earplug. That completes your 'detector assembly.' Don't use a 1N914 silicon diode; it requires too strong a signal from your radio station. If you can't obtain a 1N34, ask your parts store clerk for a germanium diode; any of them will do nicely.

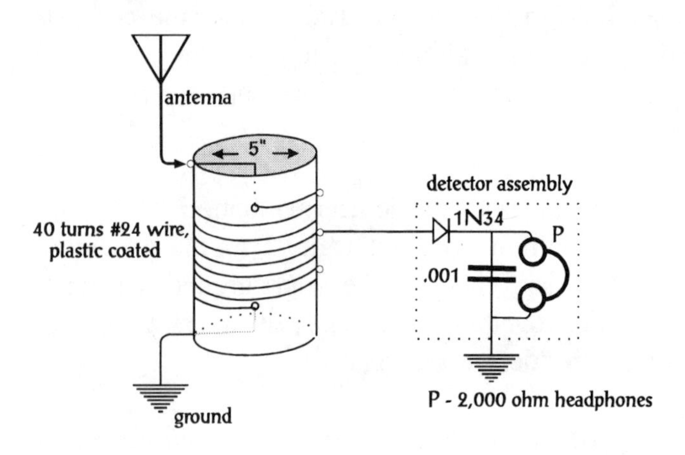

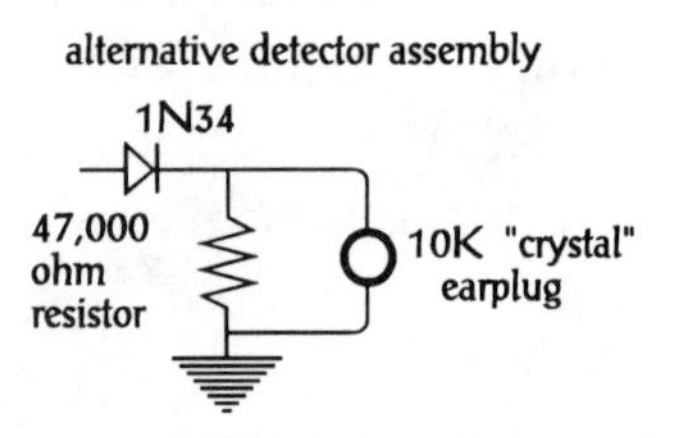

Figure 6: Crystal Set Plans

step 6 _____. Solder one end of the detector assembly to the ground wire coming out of the bottom of you oat box.

step 7 _____. Solder the other end of the assembly, to the eyelet that is half-way down the oat box coil. You can move this connection later if need be.

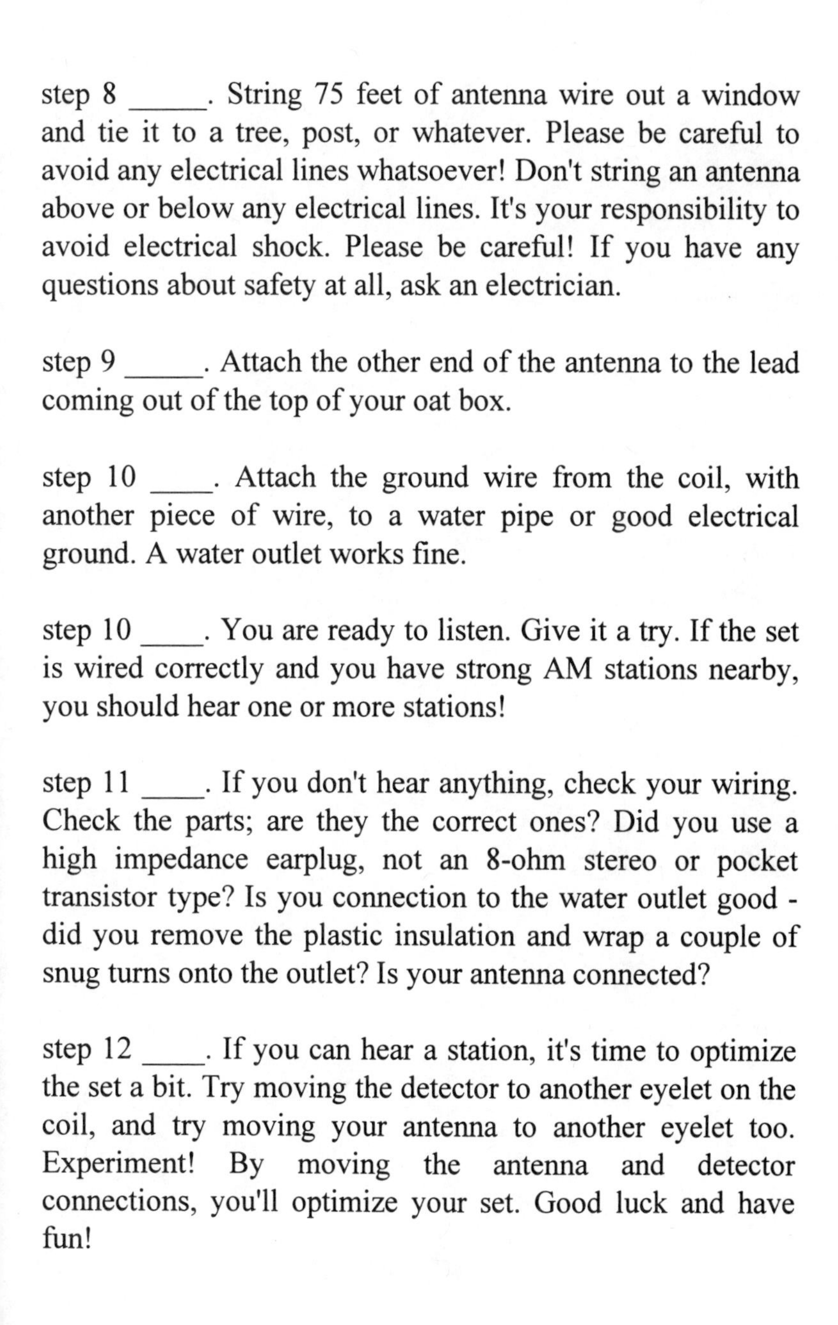

step 8 _____. String 75 feet of antenna wire out a window and tie it to a tree, post, or whatever. Please be careful to avoid any electrical lines whatsoever! Don't string an antenna above or below any electrical lines. It's your responsibility to avoid electrical shock. Please be careful! If you have any questions about safety at all, ask an electrician.

step 9 _____. Attach the other end of the antenna to the lead coming out of the top of your oat box.

step 10 ____. Attach the ground wire from the coil, with another piece of wire, to a water pipe or good electrical ground. A water outlet works fine.

step 10 ____. You are ready to listen. Give it a try. If the set is wired correctly and you have strong AM stations nearby, you should hear one or more stations!

step 11 ____. If you don't hear anything, check your wiring. Check the parts; are they the correct ones? Did you use a high impedance earplug, not an 8-ohm stereo or pocket transistor type? Is you connection to the water outlet good - did you remove the plastic insulation and wrap a couple of snug turns onto the outlet? Is your antenna connected?

step 12 ____. If you can hear a station, it's time to optimize the set a bit. Try moving the detector to another eyelet on the coil, and try moving your antenna to another eyelet too. Experiment! By moving the antenna and detector connections, you'll optimize your set. Good luck and have fun!

CHAPTER 1

JULY 1993 NEWSLETTER

IN THIS ISSUE (#13):

.Who Invented Crystal Radio?
.Tidbits...
.Membership Correspondence
.The Tikker Detector Revisited

WHO INVENTED CRYSTAL RADIO?

by Jerome N. Goggin
Claremont, NH

In response to the question, "Who made the first crystal set?" (March '93 issue), the answer is Dr. Greenleaf Whittier Pickard. And he did so on October 16, 1902! The source of this bit of trivia is an excellent article on crystal detectors by Jordan McQuay which appeared in the July 1948 issue of *Radio-Craft* magazine. Two other articles in a series on this subject appeared the following two months. Below is an excerpt from the July issue:

"At first it was a case of trial and error," relates Dr. Pickard, now 70 years old and still active as a consulting radio engineer. "After building my own test instruments, I began experiments in the summer of 1902. I started with a typical carbon-steel detector using a local battery and tried all possible variations to improve reception. One day I obtained the best results when I used an oxidized steel surface, instead of carbon, in contact with a steel needle." This occurred on July 25, 1902.

After exhausting the possibilities of the carbon-steel device as an efficient rectifier, Pickard was ready to explore further the field of minerals. Recalling his fair results with an oxidized steel surface (essentially an oxide of iron or layer of magnetite), Pickard obtained a small quantity of lodestone or natural magnetite.

"For my experiment," states Dr. Pickard, "I used a fragment of lodestone about 1/10 inch thick placed on a piece of tinfoil to provide a large contact area. A copper wire served as the second member of the contact."

On October 16, 1902, this combination was used successfully for the first time as a detector without a battery in a simple receiving circuit. Despite only fair results, this was actually the first use of a mineral-type contact detector for the reception of radio waves. Although Pickard made no attempt to patent his discovery of the magnetite detector, the date of this experiment precedes by four years the issuance of the first detector patent [awarded to Pickard in 1906 for his invention of the silicon detector] and by at least three years the activities of any other experimenter engaged in similar work. This is substantiated by Pickard's notes and other data on file in the U.S. Patent Office.

Dr. Pickard continued his experiments with minerals for more than a decade, performing over 30,000 tests and discovering more than 250 minerals suitable as detectors - including silicon and galena. Why he did not patent a galena detector is an unanswered question. But over his lifetime Dr. Pickard was awarded more than 100 patents which include:

patent#	year	invention
786,148	1905	Signal System Electrical Railways
836,531	1906	Silicon Detector
886,154	1908	Pericon Detector
888,191	1908	Improved Silicon Detector
904,222	1908	Molybdenum Detector
912,726	1909	Zincite-Chalcopyrite Detector
1,472,342	1923	Electromagnetic Compass
1,744,838	1930	Phonographic Machine

Dr. Pickard, a grand-nephew of poet John Greenleaf Whittier, was born in 1877 in Portland, Maine and died in 1956 in Newton, Massachusetts. He was educated at Harvard and M.I.T. Dr. Pickard was among the first to transmit human voice using radio waves, doing so over a distance of 10.8 miles in 1899! While experimenting with crystal detectors on his own, Dr. Pickard also worked for AT&T., where he contributed to the development of the radiophone. After inventing the silicon detector, Dr. Pickard went into business for himself, organizing the Wireless Specialty Apparatus Company, incorporated to sell his various inventions. In later years he was a consulting engineer, specializing in UHF and FM. A recognized authority on radio, Dr. Pickard also served for a time as president of the Institute of Radio Engineers. Sources of additional information on his life are *Radio's 100 Men of Science* by Orrin E. Dunlap (Harper & Brothers, 1944) and the Encyclopedia Britannica.

Two other names associated with early crystal detectors are L.W. Austin and General H.H.C. Dunwoody. Austin received two patents, one in 1906 for a holder and the other in 1907 for a tellurium/silicon "thermocouple" detector. Neither invention was successful.

General Dunwoody, retired from the U.S. Army Signal Corps, received a patent for a carborundum detector only a month after Dr. Pickard received his patent for the silicon detector. He sold his idea, however, to the American de Forest Wireless Telegraph Company (soon to become the United Wireless Telegraph Company when Lee de Forest resigned in late 1906.) The company then engaged Dr. Pickard to perfect General Dunwoody's invention, which had failed to meet initial expectations. Dr. Pickard did so by designing a new holder for the carborundum crystal. This detector, which was both rugged and stable, became very popular, especially for maritime use. By 1910 United Wireless had seventy land stations communicating with 400 ships. How the company went broke by June of that year and how the "audion" vacuum tube, invented by Lee de Forest in 1906, ultimately eclipsed all other detectors are stories well told and worth reading in *Empire of the Air* by Tom Lewis (Harper Collins, 1991).

In closing, I would like to quote two more paragraphs appearing in the *Radio-Craft* article. The first is a teaser, the second prophetic.

Pickard was successful in producing oscillations with a crystal detector circuit, so that the circuit could be operated as a beat receiver. This sounds very interesting. I only wish the author had recorded how this was done!

Dr. Pickard believes today that many of the useful radio and electrical possibilities of minerals and crystals have yet to be explored and developed. "Any contact which doesn't obey

Ohm's Law can be made to produce oscillations." states Dr. Pickard. "If it can be made to oscillate, a crystal rectifier can also be made to amplify - although the simple contact must be changed to something more complex."

That was 1948, and the world stood on the threshold of a new invention - the transistor! I wonder if, forty five years later, Dr. Pickard would feel his prophesy fulfilled. Or, would he believe that crystals and minerals still have possibilities waiting to be explored.

TIDBITS....

It's likely that an end-fed wire antenna is used with most crystal sets. For the newcomer or uninitiated, it would not occur to them to use a dipole or to wire an antenna from anywhere other than one end. In addition, most crystal sets do not have complete 'antenna tuners' built in. Further, the impedance of an end-fed wire antenna varies considerably with frequency. Consequently, while the operator may be unaware, the end-fed may compromise crystal set operation if not tuned or adjusted in length and/or position above ground for a particular frequency of operation.

While we do have a general idea of the impedance of end-feds, particularly a quarter-wave vertical above a good ground, it would be nice to know the impedance value more closely in a given installation. An antenna tuner could then be added to the set to optimize selectivity and reception. Antenna tuners for the BC and HF bands are easy to build, and schematics abound in the handbooks. The tough job is to build an inexpensive impedance bridge or alternative device to measure the resistance and reactance of the end-fed antenna.

Over the last month, I've built a few RX-Noise bridges and they seem to do a reasonable job. I'll plan on reporting schematics and results in a future issue. One drawback of an RX-Noise bridge is that a modern communications receiver is required to tune for a null. We'll look for some alternatives.

An end-fed used for HF reception, depending on length and frequency of operation, can have a resistive component varying from as low as 50 ohms to as high as 2,000 ohms or more and a reactive component with a value as high as 1,000 ohms (equivalent to several hundred puffs of capacitance at 5 Mhz with the right antenna length.)

MEMBERSHIP CORRESPONDENCE....

Vince Vigus, W6ZKZ, reports to us on a British magazine article he discovered entitled "Crystal Receiver with Self-Powered Transistor Amplifier." The article was written by J.M. Osberne, G3HMO, and appeared in the July, 1956 issue of *The Short Wave Magazine*. While the article, given the date, was intended to promote the capabilities of the transistor, our interest is, of course, peaked by the inclusion of the crystal set! The title of the article is accurate; the article describes the author's attempts to build a crystal set that derives enough power from an AM radio signal to self-power a transistor amplifier with speaker!

Mr. Osberne's solution is to build two crystal sets: one tightly coupled to the antenna and tuned to the strongest station for power, and a second, loosely coupled that tunes the desired station for listening (see Figure 1-1). He points out that such a set is only possible if the local station is strong enough and if proper filtering is carried out. The crystal set developing the power must filter out the music or voice to provide a steady DC supply for the transistor amplifier. The listening crystal set then simply does its normal job (tuning and selectivity), and supplies an audio signal to the amplifier which drives a speaker. Mr. Osberne reports that his local AM station was capable of providing 1 milliampere (ma) of current into a 5000 ohm load (that's 5 milliwatts of power), sufficient to operate a simple transistor amplifier and speaker.

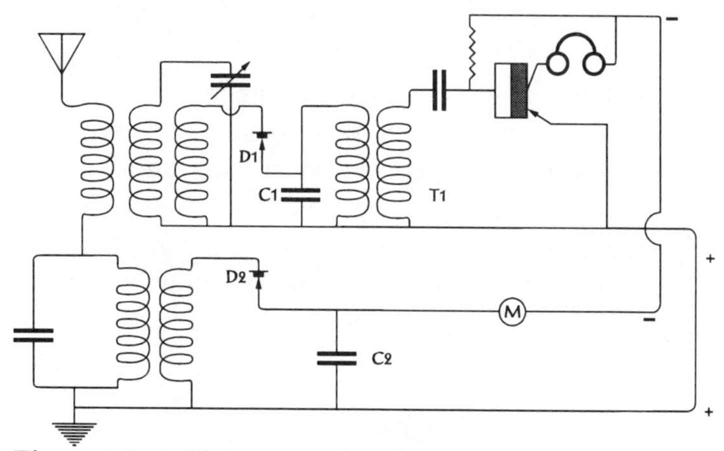

Figure 1-1: Self-Powered Receiver

In Figure 1-1, the bottom crystal set is the DC supply. Capacitor C2 needs to be 10 μfd or so to filter out modulation coming from the local AM station, and the antenna is tightly coupled. The corresponding detector capacitor in the 'listening' set is labeled C1; its value is the usual .001 μfd (1000 puff). Transformer T1 provides a match between the detector output and the low impedance transistor base. The antenna is loosely coupled, preserving selectivity.

Mr. Osberne closes with a neat comment, "There is no great deal to be gained, theoretically, by using this set, transistor amplified, on the strongest local station except for good selectivity. But with sufficient power gain in the audio stage *every* signal (other more distant stations) could theoretically be brought up to the level of the local, which is where the advantage lies."

David Hays, KØKD, Great Bend, KS, reports the following: "Here is what I've heard so far on my xtal set. I'm really impressed. Now, if I can build a wave trap that will attenuate our local AM station during daylight hours - I can copy some more regional stations. My antenna is a 130' end-fed wire. I have two copper clad 8 foot ground rods to act as an RF ground. Listening to radio activity on a crystal set is a lot of fun and I'm amazed by the results! 73s - Dave." [editor: Dave logged most of the following during early hours, 5 AM. Was your local station off then Dave, and which crystal set design did you use? - Nice job!]

freq	call	location
1590	KGVB	Great Bend, KS
1520	KOMA	Okla City, OK
1290	KWLS	Pratt, KS
1200	WOAI	San Antonio, TX
1170	KVOO	Tulsa, OK
1120	KMOX	St. Louis, MO
1080	KRLD	Dallas, TX
990	KRSL	Russell, KS
910	KINA	Salina, KS
880	KRVN	Lexington, NE
870	WWL	New Orleans, LA

850	KOA	Denver, CO
830	WCTO	Minneapolis, MN
820	WBAP	Forth Worth, TX
790	KXXX	Colby, KS
690	KGGF	Coffeyville, KS
680	WBBM	Chicago, IL
620	KWFT	Wichita Falls, TX
580	WIBW	Topeka, KS

P.A. Kinzie, Kingman, AZ, sent me a note, expressing interest and thanks for the articles on the Miller 595 Tuner. In addition he sent along a two-part article he wrote for the *Arizona Antique Radio Club News*, Vol. IX, No. 1, Spring, 1992, entitled "The Crystal Detector: It's Development and Applications." The articles are interesting and compliment the Goggin article in this issue. Perhaps we'll have room to include this two-part series or portions of it in an upcoming issue.

Larry Waggoner, Wichita KS, sent me eight "M.R.L. handbooks that might be of crystal set interest to you." Thanks Larry. Elmer Osterhoudt's Modern Radio Labs (MRL) stuff is interesting; some of the booklets are new to me. [Note: Elmer wrote these 20-30 page booklets in the late 1940s and early 1950s. HB-1 has a 1949 copyright date.]

MRL-18	(HB-25) Crystal Set Circuits
MRL-2	Long Distance Crystal Sets
HB-3	Crystal Detectors
HB-10	Facts for Crystal Experimenters
HB-1	Headphones: Operation & Repair
HB-6	How to Make Coils
HB-5	Crystal Set Construction
HB-17	(MRL-20) Crystal Set Circuits

Del Tysdal, Fargo, ND, sent along a copy of an article entitled "In Justice of the Crystal Set," an interview of Dr. Greenleaf W. Pickard appearing in *Popular Science Monthly*, September 1922. Pickard states, "Already, we can confidently estimate that of perhaps 2,000,000 receiving sets in the United States, a majority use galena for detection."

Oatmeal box again:

Bob Zirkelbach, Pleasant Hill, CA reports, "I have 8 home-brew xtal sets and my favorite is the MRL No. 2 Long Distance Set. He also stated, "I think my first crystal set was a Quaker Oats box set. Mine was similar to the plans enclosed, which were in the '*Pro-phy-lac-tic (toothpaste!) Handy Book for Boys*,' a 1923 copy. It was reprinted in an issue of *Monitoring Times* some years ago." He also noted our article in the May issue on the Italian VAAM detectors, and points out that these are available from Antique Electronic Supply.

The copy of the 'plans enclosed' is hard to read so we'll not reproduce it here. However, the set centers around the Quaker Oats box and the coil wound on it. If you want to try such a set, the cardboard tube is specified to be 4 inches in diameter and at least 5 inches high. The main coil should be seventy turns of No. 22 double cotton covered (WCC) magnet wire, tapped every ten turns. The antenna pickup coil is specified as 8 turns with a tap at every turn. The usual detector and headphones then attach as desired. No mention of a tuning capacitor is made. The coil is self-resonant; that is, the coil windings provide their own capacitance. Checking this out would be a fun project. Does anyone have more details on this, or does anyone have a copy of the

Monitoring Times reprint? I'll write Bob Grove in Brasstown, NC.

THE TIKKER DETECTOR REVISITED
or A Receiver for Continuous Waves

By Phil Anderson, WØXI

Having built a number of crystal sets for AM broadcast band listening (medium frequencies, 550-1600 Khz), my interest has turned to experimenting with crystal sets for shortwave reception (high frequencies, 3-30 Mhz). While my initial attempts have been satisfying, because I easily picked up strong AM broadcasts in the International AM Broadcast bands (5.950-6.200 and 9.500-9.775 Mhz), I have wanted to build more sensitive and selective sets. In addition, I've had the notion that building a crystal set for CW reception and code practice would be fun.

With these desires, it seemed that searching for better detectors might be a place to start. Hence, over the last six months or so, as time permitted, I've looked at the coherer, biasing diodes for weaker signal detection, the electrolytic detector, and the Poulsen Tikker detector. In the January issue of this newsletter I posed a mystery question, "I ran across a bit on the Poulsen tikker detector. Can anybody tell me what it is?" In response, Jerome Goggin, Claremont, NH, submitted a nice article on the Tikker which, you may recall, was printed in the March issue.

As with all investigations, this too was heuristic; that is, a question always leads to other questions and ideas. Of course, that's the fun of it! After reading Goggin's article, I could not figure out exactly how the Tikker worked. If it didn't detect audio in the usual sense that AM diode detectors do (rectification), how did it work? How could the Tikker sample an RF parallel-tuned circuit (tank circuit) and come away with audio? This seemed like magic and a challenge!

At nearly the same time, I received a copy of *Practical Wireless Telegraphy*, by Elmer Bucher (1917). Bucher was an Instructing Engineer at the Marconi Wireless Telegraph Co. This book opened new vistas for me! [As John Gibson, Berkeley, CA, says, "All crystal set builders should have a copy of *Practical Wireless Telegraphy*."] This text covers

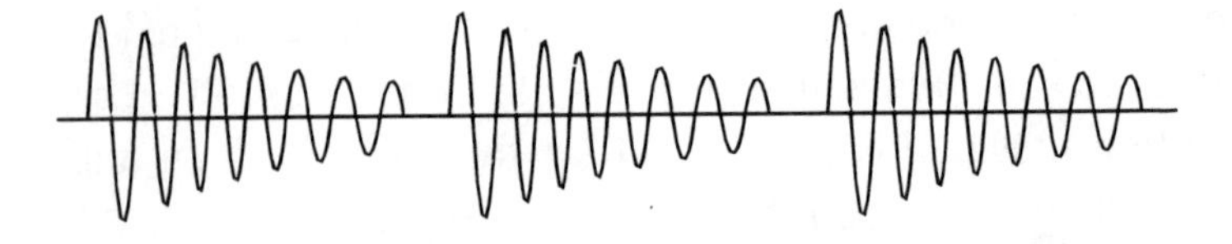

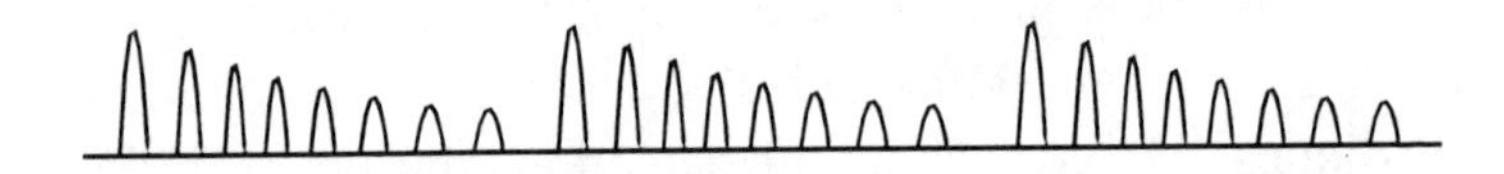

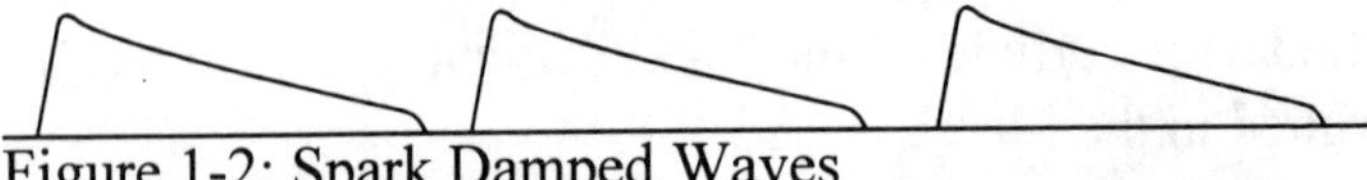

Figure 1-2: Spark Damped Waves

spark transmitters, CW spark receivers, Marconi receiving sets, and transmitters and receivers for undamped waves.

Early spark systems used damped waves; hence the usual crystal detector worked for reception. Each spark created a burst of energy which was filtered by the transmitter L-C circuit. This circuit determined the frequency of the damped oscillations and the rate of damping. When a basic crystal receiver, as shown in Figure 1-3, received the damped wave, it was rectified. These pulses were then filtered and heard as audio 'sawtooth waves' in the headphones.

However, the damped wave spark transmitters were slowly replaced with transmitters that produced undamped (continuous) waves, like those transmitted today. In addition, since an AM detector cannot demodulate a continuous wave into an audio tone, designers during

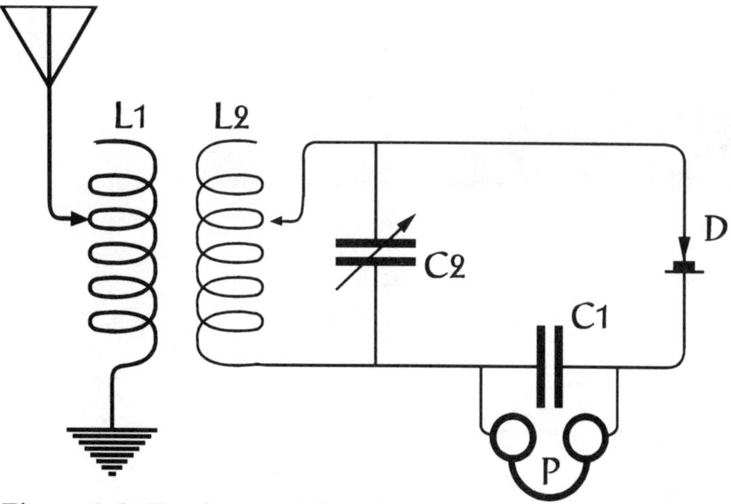

Figure 1-3: Fundamental Receiver

Bucher's time were faced with the challenge of creating another kind of detector. Bucher describes this as "The Problem" in Part XV of *Practical Wireless Telegraphy*.

In describing The Problem and the Tikker, he said, "If an ordinary crystal rectifier is connected to a receiving set tuned to a continuous wave transmitter, owing to the lack of discontinuity in the advancing wave, a pulsating current flows through the receiving telephone. These pulsations take place at such rapid rates that the diaphragm of the telephone is either held down continuously or repelled continuously resulting in no sound except at the beginning or end of the flow.... To make undamped oscillations audible, we are

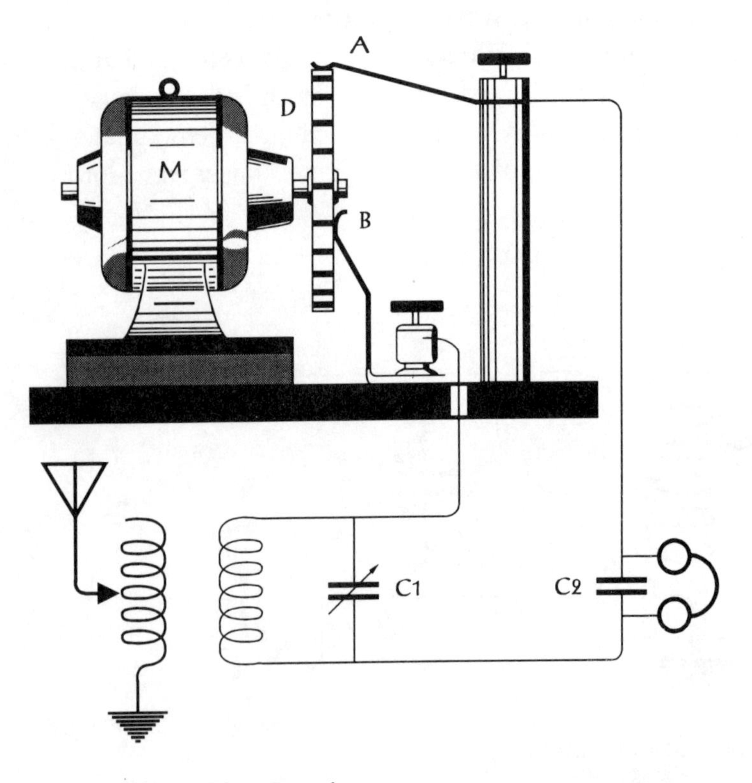

Figure 1-4: Tikker Receiver

compelled to break up the oscillations of either the transmitter or receiver into *groups* suitable for maximum response in the head telephone or to supply other means at the receiver to make them audible. The receivers at present in use [that work] are: (1) The Poulsen Tikker or chopper; (2) The heterodyne system; (3) The Goldschmidt Tone Wheel; (4) The Regenerative Vacuum Valve (beat receiver)."

He goes on to describe each of these in turn. We have reproduced the diagram of the Poulsen Tikker in Figure 1-4. In his words, "A disc D mounted on the shaft of the motor M has a number of teeth filled in between...The radio-frequent currents flow from brush B to A through the disc which interrupts them from 300 to 1000 times per second. The charge built up in condenser C-1...discharges into the telephone condenser C-2, at regular intervals. C-2 in turn discharges through the head telephone creating a single sound for the charge accumulated. Due to the fact that the Tikker discharges C-1 at various potentials, a non-uniform note (pitch) is produced lacking the desired musical pitch for reading through atmospheric electricity. However, the Tikker suffices as a simple receiver and good results have been obtained by its use at several ship and shore stations."

discovery....

After reading Bucher's text, I was still not sure exactly how the Tikker worked. Hence, I decided to build one, using modern circuits, to see exactly how it worked. I still had the hope and the notion that, if indeed it worked, it would produce audio signals in the headphones below the threshold of the usual crystal detector circuit, i.e. a 1N34 diode. Once built and tested, Bucher's text and the Tikker's operation became clear!

To build a modern day Tikker, I used a 555 IC timer in place of the motor timing wheel. In addition, to substitute for the contacts on the disc, I used a 4066 IC switch. The remainder of my modern day Tikker receiver is essentially identical to his.

facts from the past....

Before describing the operation of this circuit, a few points of clarification are in order. Even after building the circuit, it's operation was not immediately clear to me until I read the rest of Elmer's book. Bucher said at the beginning of Part VI, "The electrical waves for commercial wireless telegraphy are set into motion by alternating currents at frequencies varying from 25,000 to 1,000,000 cycles per second. We shall confine this chapter to an explanation of the apparatus for the production of *damped electrical oscillations [spark]* which are employed almost universally for wireless ship to shore communications." Further, on page 284, I noted he wrote, "To illustrate its mode of operation we may assume that signals are being received from the high-power station at Tuckerton, New Jersey, the normal wavelength of which is 7,400 meters corresponding to an oscillation frequency of 40,540 cycles per second."

the radio carrier was at 40,540 cycles!

That means that coil values were very large and/or tuned circuit capacitance values could also be large; the radio frequency was *so low*!

My modern day Tikker detector is shown in Figure 1-5. An IFR signal generator was used as the signal source. The usual crystal set tuned circuit (tank circuit) is next. Note that the coil has a value of one millihenry, and the main capacitor is .01 μfd. Next, the Tikker wheel is replaced by a 4066 analog switch that turns on and off at the rate supplied by the 555 timer, at control pin 13. The output of the tikker is exactly the same as Bucher's; it consists of a .01 μfd capacitor and a pair of 4,000 ohm headphones [mine are Russian.]

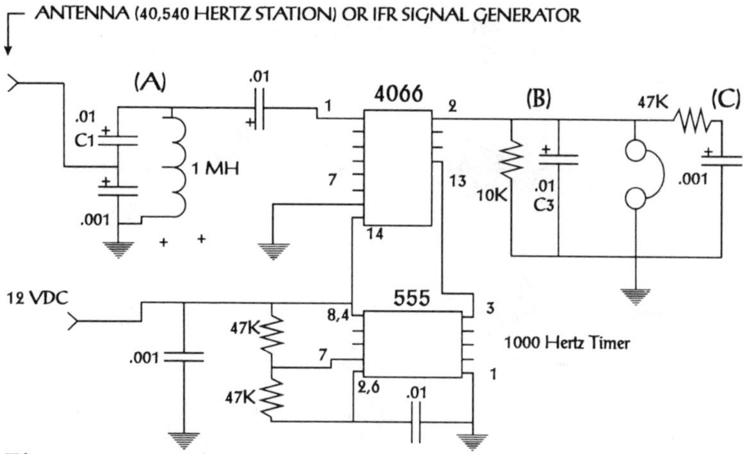

Figure 1-5: Modern Day Tikker

operation of the modern day tikker

First, the resistor and cap values for the 555 timer are set so that it produces a square-wave at 1000 hertz. With this control voltage, the 4066 switch turns on and off 1000 times per second, staying on each time for 1/2 millisecond. While the switch is on, due to its very low on resistance, the .01 μfd cap and headphone are, effectively, placed in parallel with the .01 μfd cap in the input RF circuit. Hence, if the generator is tuned to the frequency that is resonant with both C1 and the one millihenry coil, the oscillations build to a maximum. The headphone has a DC resistance of 4,000 ohms and an inductive reactance about the same at 1000 hertz; hence, the inductance of the headphone is large compared to the L of the tank circuit - thereby not affecting it.

When the 4066 turns off, the charge remaining on C3 discharges through the headphones, and the result is a tone that is approximately 1000 cycles in pitch. The oscilloscope traces I obtained, corresponding to points A, B, and C in the schematic (Figure 1-5), are shown in Figure 1-6.

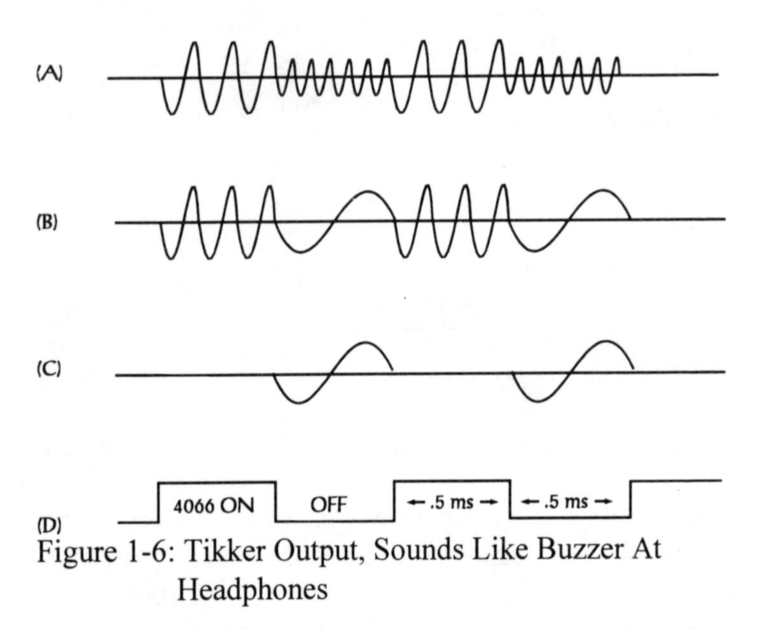

Figure 1-6: Tikker Output, Sounds Like Buzzer At Headphones

It is interesting to note that since the 555 timer and the IFR generator are not synchronized the amount of charge on C1 and C3 (equal since they have the same μfd value) will vary at the instant the 4066 opens up, leaving half the total charge on C3 to dissipate through the headphones. This creates a kind of grainy sound.

Finally, I was surprised that I could hear tones, by toggling the IFR generator, when signals as small as 10 millivolts were supplied to this modern day tikker set. There is no 1N34 diode threshold to overcome! In hindsight, considering the human ear is as sensitive as a VHF 2-meter receiver, but of course at different frequencies, it is not all that amazing. In summary, the tikker samples a part of the energy from the input tuned circuit, and then discharges it through the headphones. The rate is fast enough that CW (Morse Code) is still heard. Just amazing. It remains to be seen if we can convert this receiver of 40,540 Hertz to one for listening to, say, 3.5 Mhz (amateur code)! We'll try.

CHAPTER 2

SEPTEMBER 1993 NEWSLETTER

IN THIS ISSUE (#14):

.The Simplest Crystal Set
.Tidbits...
.References
.Membership Correspondence
.Vendors

THE SIMPLEST CRYSTAL SET!

Phil Anderson, WØXI

After spending an evening recently reading Elmer Bucher's *Practical Wireless Telegraphy* (1917), I decided to experiment with the basic crystal set pictured in Figure 2-1. The set consists of an antenna, an antenna inductor, the detector and headphones.

In my first attempt I wired the set without the antenna inductor (coil) that Bucher refers to as the "aerial tuning inductance." Without that coil, and not counting the antenna as a part of the set, I had a crystal receiver with just two parts, the detector and the headphones! It was 10:00 PM when I put the phones on and the Christian Science Monitor, broadcasting on 9.5 Mhz from the east coast, came right through! Volume was good, probably due to the fact that my end-fed wire antenna was close to resonance for that frequency (one-half wavelength at 50 feet).

Since my two-part set had no selectivity I was not surprised to hear other stations! There was a weak one that I could barely hear but recognized as my local AM station on 1320 kilohertz. Knowing that the antenna was capacitive at 1320

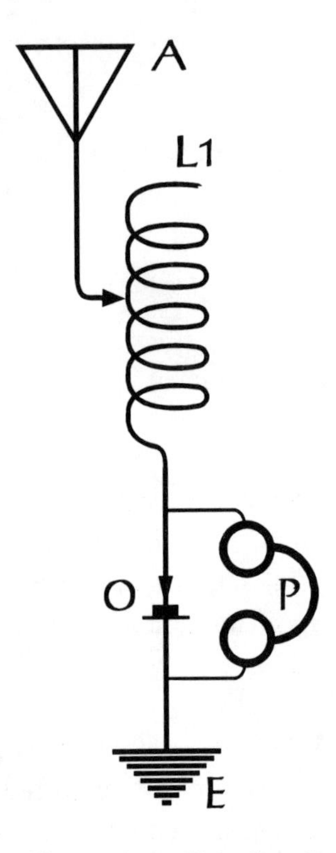

Figure 2-1: Simplest Radio Receiver

kilohertz, much shorter than a quarter-wavelength, I attached a 60 turn, 2 inch diameter coil in series with the antenna. As I expected, the local AM signal increased markedly in volume. I had resonated the antenna to the frequency of operation and increased the current flowing through the diode, as Elmer Bucher advised in his book.

Elmer explains this basic circuit as follows. "The circuits of a simple radio receiver appear in the diagram [Figure 2-1], wherein a *crystal rectifier O*, connected in series with the antenna A, is shunted by the *receiving telephone P*.

"The action of this apparatus during the reception of signals may be explained as follows: A train of waves radiated by the transmitter induces an alternating current in the aerial circuit which will flow freely through the crystal in one direction, but will be opposed in the opposite direction. In one direction the current passes from the earth upward through the crystal, and thus places a charge on the aerial wires. The return current is opposed; hence the rectified oscillations (for each spark of the transmitter) accumulate a charge on the antenna wires, which at the termination of a wave train leaks to earth through the head telephone, creating a single sound for each group of incoming oscillations.

"Because of its resistance, the crystal impedes the free flow of oscillations and, to some extent, destroys the *tuning qualities* of the aerial circuit. Hence, to enhance the tuning properties of the antenna system, the crystal is removed therefrom and connected in a second circuit, termed the *local detector* circuit."

simple radio circuit alternatives

While Bucher's set shows the diode and headphones in parallel, several alternatives exist. Another basic set puts the diode and headphones is series and places a .001 µµfd capacitor across the headphone leads. I've not tried this method yet.

Still another set, shown in Figure 2-2, wires the antenna coil (A) directly to ground and places the diode (D), headphones (P), and capacitor (C1) in parallel with it. This set has a great advantage over the set in Figure 2-1; the voltage available for the diode is greatly increased! In Figure 2-1, the antenna and antenna coil form an equivalent R-C-L series tuned circuit. R represents the radiation resistance of the antenna, and C is the capacitance of the antenna (assuming an end-fed wire less than one-quarter wavelength). L is then picked to

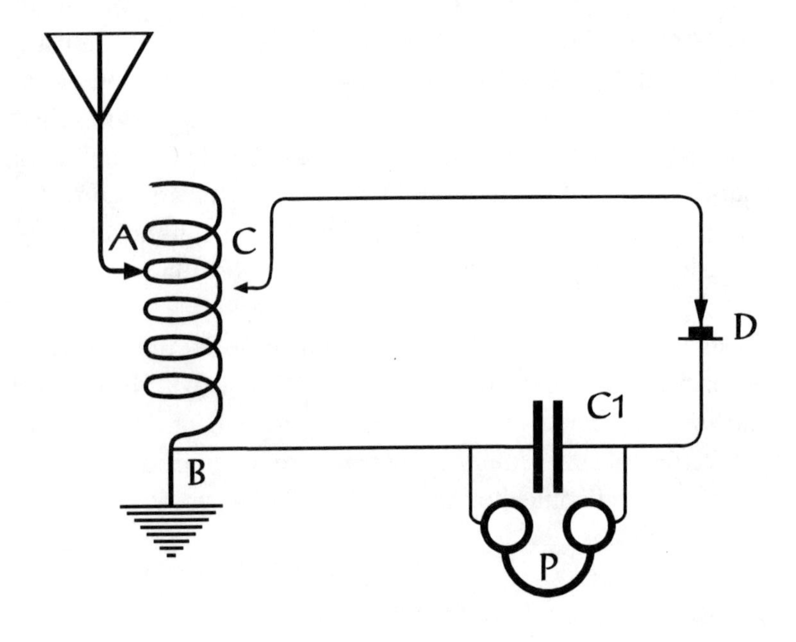

resonate with C, reducing the C-L series impedance to near zero, thereby increasing diode current to a maximum. However, voltage is still low. In Figure 2-2 the antenna and antenna coil still form the same R-C-L series circuit, but this time the diode picks off the voltage *at the center* of the series tuned circuit, between C and L. At this point, the voltage is large, boosted by roughly the ratio of the coil reactance to R, the antenna resistance.

As you may recall, the quality factor of a series circuit Q_S is defined as the ratio of the coil reactance to the circuit resistance.

$$Q_S = \frac{(2 \cdot \pi \cdot f \cdot L)}{R} \qquad Q_S = \frac{X}{R}$$

f = frequency (hertz)
L = inductance (henrys)
X = inductive reactance (ohms)
R = series resistance (ohms)

Hence, if the R-C-L circuit is resonant and the Q is large, then the voltage across the coil is boosted, making diode detection easier, particularly for weak signals. Thinking of this another way, at resonance, the voltage of the antenna generates a current through the R-C-L series circuit; C and L, in series, present zero impedance to the signal. Hence, the AC (RF) current is roughly,

$$I = \frac{V_{\text{antenna}}}{R_{\text{antenna}}}$$

Assuming that the detector is attached to the top of the coil, a voltage is developed by that same current through the coil! Hence, the voltage at the detector is higher.

$$V_{\text{coil}} = I \cdot X = \frac{V_{\text{antenna}}}{R} \cdot X$$

$$V_{\text{coil}} = V_{\text{antenna}} \cdot Q_S$$

We wired the set of Figure 2-2 for our local AM station and noted a considerable boost in signal as expected.

more selectivity

Figure 2-3 displays the next step up in set complexity, adding the familiar "local detector" circuit. This schematic probably looks more familiar to you as the traditional crystal radio set. The second tuned circuit provides added selectivity and isolation from antenna variations.

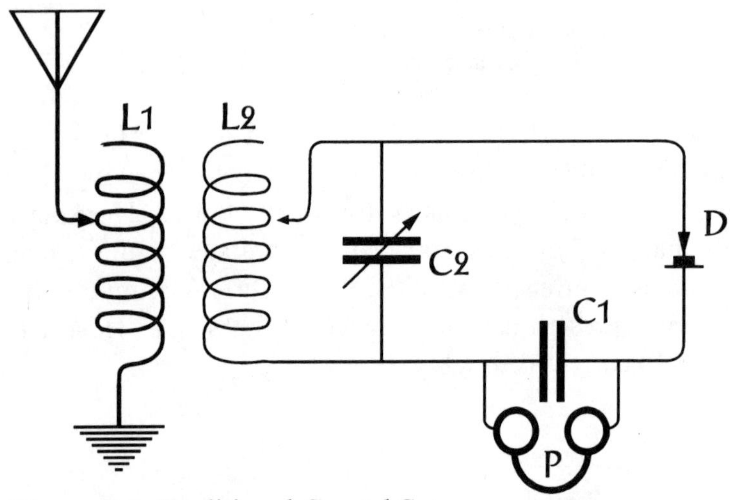

Figure 2-3: Traditional Crystal Set

try the simple radio receiver

If you decide the try the circuits in Figures 2-1 and 2-2, I recommend that you use an end-fed antenna of roughly 180 feet for the BC band. Reduce the antenna length to 50 feet when DXing the shortwave bands. You'll have to experiment with antenna coil values in order to resonate the antenna for maximum reception. Without knowing the exact capacitance of the antenna, you can still successfully tune it by adding a small valued capacitor (say 75 pf) in series with the antenna and the antenna coil. In this case, calculate the inductance of the antenna coil based on the value of added C for the frequency of operation desired. (By adding a small series cap, you've forced the capacitance of the antenna to be small). Have fun!

TIDBITS....

Dean Manley, KH6B, Hilo, Hawaii, wire abbreviations:
s.s.c. = single silk covered
d.s.c. = double silk covered
s.c.c. = single cotton covered
d.c.c. = double cotton covered

Richard Briggs, Haydenville, MA, "Phil, just got your newsletter, TERRIFIC!"

Scott Stevens, Baltimore, MD, "Since most old time radio clubs involve themselves with tube/transistor radios, I look forward to learning more about the Xtal Society that can help me pursue an aspect of the radio hobby closer to my heart."

Gary Housholder, Dunbar, WV, Gary mentions he has a Crosley V (1914). He also stated, "...have done a lot of research into the Tesla studies and we are still doing some research in VLF and the natural wobble of this great earth." Gary! What is this wobble stuff; sounds interesting?

rocket radio

Jim Clark, Mesa AZ, "Regarding the note from Sallie Stout in El Paso asking if anyone remembers the rocket-ship crystal radios from the 50s [May 93 newsletter p.3], I ran across one of these in an antique store this past weekend. It was in dead mint condition - the radio had never been removed from its sealed plastic bag, and the very colorful box was perfect. The box was labeled 'Rocket Radio,' and it was made by Miniman Co. Ltd. - the model number was MG-305. The price? Only $75.00. How times do change...."

MEMBERSHIP CORRESPONDENCE....

What do John Collins, Jerome Goggin, and Phil Anderson have in common? You might guess that we are all crystal set enthusiasts. That is true; however, what I had in mind was that all three of us buy books from Rainy Day Books in NH. As I understand it, John and Jerome met there by accident. I, of course, purchase by mail, way out here in "Dorothy-Tornado Alley" land. John reports that he too is now the proud owner of a copy of *Practical Wireless Telegraphy* by Elmer Bucher. He says, "You were right Phil, everyone who plays with crystal sets should have a copy. I've been having a great time tracing through the Marconi sets and thinking 'wouldn't it be great to build something that looks like that!'"

HF crystal set

Over the past month, John Collins and I have been trading notes on coils, coil "Q," and HF crystal sets. John states, "My Short Wave Crystal Set coil is 10 turns of #12 silver-plated wire, 3 inches in diameter, and 2 inches long. It's tuned with a 100 pf cap from 5.5 to about 15 Mhz. The antenna is fed via a 'swinging link' for adjustable coupling. The detector is tapped one, two, or three turns from ground for variable loading. The circuit 'Q' is about 500 (3dB bandwidth of 12 Khz at 6 Mhz), and selectivity is pretty good!" He noted that the set is fed by 75 feet of open wire line attached to a 140 foot dipole. He uses a balanced link-coupled tuner to "resonate" the antenna. (John, I hope I got the circuit right from your description of the set. I assume that you mean by "swinging link" that the antenna coil can be slid away from or brought closer to the tuned circuit coil to adjust coupling? Right?)

John says he has tried several diodes in parallel (4-1N82As) to lower conduction threshold. Has anyone experimented with that? We'll have to try. [John, have you tried biasing the diode(s) with a variable voltage fed through a 1 megohm resistor. Try biasing just below the 200 mV threshold - with one diode.]

John reports hearing Harvest Radio and Christian Science Monitor, both HF broadcasts, during the day and many stations at night. In Kansas, I must wait patiently for the nighttime. Then I can easily hear the Christian Science Monitor broadcasts on the 9 Mhz band.

push-pull crystal set

Ernest Rice, KA8HEB, Blanchester, OH, has recently joined our society. He noted, "I live a few miles from Cincinnati which has a 50K station, WLW, and it covers most of the dial on the simple sets. When I was young WLW was a 500K station and it covered the entire dial." He's referring of course to the wattage of the station, 50K meaning 50,000 watts of RF! Gosh Ernest, just hang a wire out the window and attach it to your diode and earphones! (see the lead article).

Ernest sent along a copy of an article entitled "Push-Pull Crystal Receiver," by Art Trauffer, originally appearing in an old issue of *Elementary Electronics*. No dates appeared on the sheets Ernest. Do you have the issue date? The subtitle for the article read, "Supersensitive circuit pulls in distant AM stations. Has a double-tuned detector and two transistors to raise signal to speaker level." The circuit presented features antenna link coupling, two separate tuned circuits, each feeding one diode, a two-transistor amplifier, and a 3000 to 8 ohm transformer for matching to a loudspeaker. There is nothing particularly new here, but the combination is nice. The tank coils are wound together on a 1 1/2 inch diameter form, using #32 enameled copper wire. The tuned circuit coils, L1 and L3, each consist of 95 turns, and are wound on opposite ends of the form. L2, the primary (or antenna pickup) coil, has 30 turns, is placed in the middle, and is separated from L1 and L3 by 1/8 inch at each end. The advantage gained by having two tuned circuits and detectors is twice the audio. Each circuit contributes equal audio energy but from opposite half-cycles of the radio signal.

William Jones reports from Sanger, CA that he got hooked on crystal sets in 1954! Supplies for early projects came from the Philmore catalog. His latest set is a "customized rendition of a design from K.E. Edwards' *Radios that Work for Free*." Bill says that he hand-crafted a variometer to serve as a variable antenna coupling link to the main tuning coil. "This radio was built inside an antique wooden box with a hinged lid, and, as much as possible, made to look like it came right off the Lemco assembly line."

oscillating crystal detectors

Vern Killion, W5UYF, Lexington, NE, sent us a few pages from the August, 1919 issue of the *Electrical Experimenter*, containing an article entitled "How I Invented the Crystal Detector (Greenleaf Whittier Pickard)." While I had seen the article before, I missed or passed over a small section with the headline "Oscillating Crystal Detectors". Here Pickard notes, "The last word on crystal detectors and their uses has yet to be written. For example, it may be of interest to know that they can be made to OSCILLATE, under proper circuit conditions, and I found it possible to receive intelligible signals from UNDAMPED wave stations across the Atlantic, on a simple contact between a fragment of galena and a fine wire." Vern noted that, perhaps, it's too bad that this "tunnel diode action" wasn't explored then in more depth. GE rediscovered it in the 50s! Sounds like that could lead to another fun project, Vern!

Vern also indicates that he's built most of the MIDCO circuits using a 1N34. He claims circuit "E" is the best. He used PVC pipe for the coil forms. [I recently questioned the lossy nature of PVC (in RF fields) but noticed after builting a coil on PVC and then as an air coil that there is no appreciable loss.]

detectus electrolyticus

Jerome Goggin, Claremont, NH. Jerome, just wondering if you ever received that Wollaston wire from Dartmouth College? It will be interesting to see if the "broken microscope" apparatus will allow you and your son to experience the operation of an electrolytic detector.

the tuggle circuit

Murray Hoover, 1042 William Street, London, Ontario, Canada, N5Y-2S9, sent us a note about the Tuggle Circuit. You may recall that we had heard about the circuit and asked

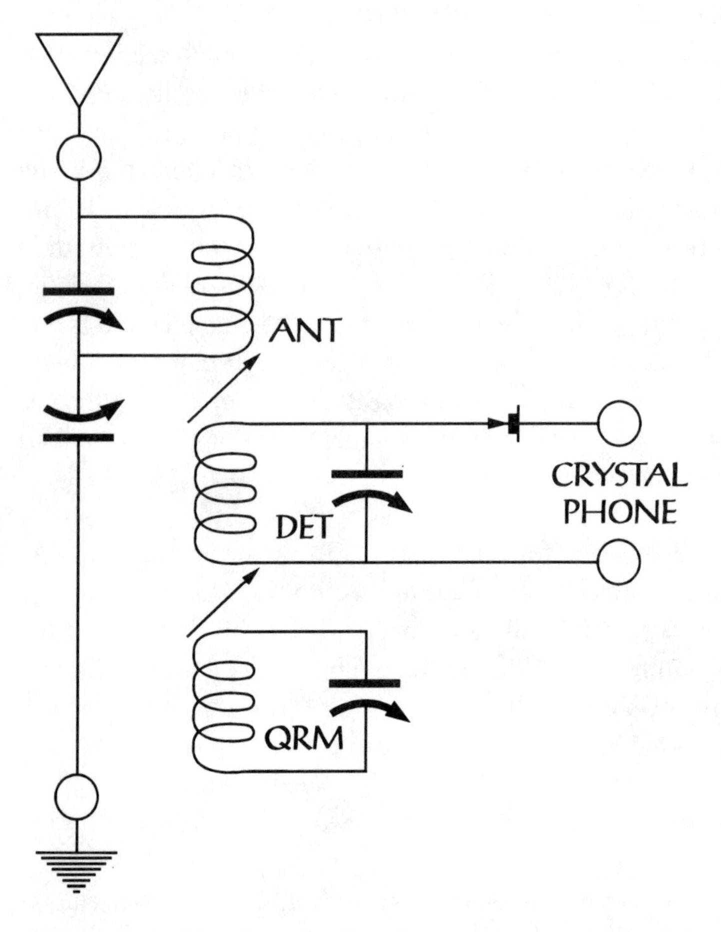

Figure 2-4: The Tuggle Circuit

members to report. A schematic of the Tuggle is shown in Figure 2-4. The note Murray sent is dated 11-28-86, and is entitled "The Tuggle Circuit," and is a National Radio Club Reprint, R-40. I am not familiar with this group. Does it still exist? Does anyone know?

The circuit is by no means unique. Many crystal sets using a "QRM" tank circuit coupled with the antenna and detector tuned circuits came long before the date listed in the reprint. It would be interesting to model the affect on one AM detector [tuned circuit and detector diode] by another tuned circuit, the Tuggle being one example. From the reprint, it appears that with the Tuggle, coupling between circuits was adjusted by sliding the antenna and QRM coils in and out. The coils were mounted on opposite ends of and in line with the detector coil.

In addition, Murray sent along a copy of an early spec. sheet (brochure) on the Miller Tuner. For the fifties the hype is pretty strong: "SENSATIONAL! is the word for the New Miller Band-Pass TRF tuner using a germanium diode detector. NO TUBES, NO POWER SUPPLY, NO HUM! A simple 2-tuned circuit negative mutual coupled band pass tuner. Simple, easy to assemble and wire."

more correspondence

Henri Chapdelaine, Manchester, NH sent us a note about his college radio. "When I was attending college, my 'clock radio' was a crystal set feeding an old horn speaker. It was tuned to WFEA, located 12 miles away, and at 6:00 AM. each morning WFEA woke us with the National Anthem!" (I wrote Henri, asking for more details on the horn speaker, as a possible project.)

CHAPTER 3

NOVEMBER 1993 NEWSLETTER

IN THIS ISSUE (#15)

.A Simple Shortwave Crystal Set
.Did Insects Beat Us To Radio?
.Tidbits...
.Membership Correspondence
.Vendors
.Society QSL Card

A SIMPLE SHORTWAVE CRYSTAL SET

Phil Anderson, WØXI

While most crystal sets built today tune the 540-1600 Khz AM broadcast band, they can be easily modified to listen to AM stations in the 3-12 Mhz high frequency (HF) band as well. Just think of it, instead of listening to your local DJ, you could - at night - tune to the Christian Science Monitor in Boston or capture international AM broadcasts! It all comes compliments of the basic crystal set, shown in Figure 3-1.

How can this be, you ask? Well, it turns out that the circuit schematics for medium-wave (MW) and HF sets are exactly the same; a crystal set is a crystal set regardless of frequency! All you need to do for set conversion is change the coil and attach a good HF antenna. I'll show you how to do that, but I'll leave construction technique and listening fun to you! Most basic MW AM sets utilize a coil of about 60 turns, 4.0 inches or so in length, and 1.5 to 2.0 inches in diameter. These dimensions result in a coil with 100-250 microhenry (μH) of inductance. The capacitor used is usually the standard air-variable type, the kind you can carve out of an old tube set from the 1950s.

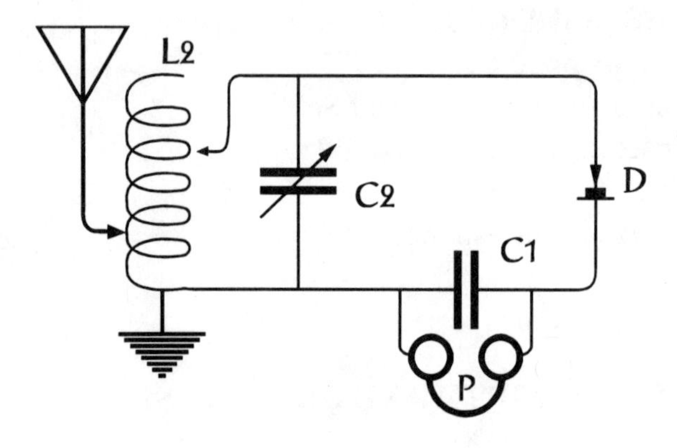

Figure 3-1: The Basic Crystal Set

the HF coil

For HF operation, an inductance of 3 to 5 μH can be used with the same tuning capacitor. Given a desired listening frequency, you can calculate the inductance of the coil by assuming a mid-range value for the tuning capacitor, say 180 picofarads (pf). Assuming 5.85 Mhz (the Christian Science Monitor frequency) the coil inductance should be about 3.5 μH. The formula for this calculation is:

$$L = \frac{1}{f^2 \cdot (4\pi)^2 \cdot C}$$

Care must be taken in designing/choosing a 3.5 μH coil; not every coil with this inductance will work well for HF reception. The capacitance of the coil must be kept low, and the quality factor 'Q' of the coil must be kept high.

By minimizing the coil capacitance, a maximum (coil) inductance can be obtained, resulting in stronger signals at the detector. In addition, at high radio frequencies the current in a coil flows only on and near the surface of the wire, a phenomenon called the skin effect. As a result the resistance in coils used at HF frequencies increases markedly. Hence, the only choice we have, if we wish to preserve the Q of the coil, is to use large wire, say #16. Then the coil resistance due to the skin effect is reduced. In turn, the spacing between coil windings should be increased so that the larger wire does not create added coil capacitance.

So where does this leave us? How can we obtain a coil of 3.5 μH with just a few turns spread out? The single-layer coil formula, shown below, provides a hint.

$$L = \frac{d^2 \cdot \text{turns}^2}{18d + 40\text{length}}$$

$d = 2.05$ inches   length $= 1.5$ inches   turns $= 9$

$L = 3.5\mu\text{H}$

Increase the diameter of the coil and limit its length. A coil with 3.5 μH is then obtained by setting the diameter at 2 inches, length at 1.5 inches, and turns at 9. Other coil designs could be devised as well.

antennas for HF operation

The easiest way to obtain satisfactory results with this simple set is to use an antenna that presents a 50 ohm load. Half-wave dipole antennas cut to length for the frequency of operation present 70 ohms of resistance, which is close enough. An alternative is to use an end-fed antenna; attach one end of a wire to the set and string the rest of the wire out over its full distance as far above ground as possible. For 5.85 Mhz - my listening frequency - I recommend an end-fed one-quarter wavelength long, or roughly 42 feet. At a quarter-wave an end-fed antenna appears resistive with no reactive impedance component, resulting in a simple antenna that will not detune your HF set.

The formula for length (L) is:

$$L = \frac{495 \cdot (.95)}{2 \cdot f} \text{ feet} \qquad \text{where } f = \text{Mhz}$$

attaching the antenna to the L-C circuit

As noted in the introduction, in addition to changing the coil in the L-C circuit (L2-C2, figure 3-2) of the basic crystal set, the other major challenge is to properly attach the antenna to the set in order to retain selectivity and at the same time maximize signal volume. One straightforward method is to attach the antenna directly to the coil of the L-C circuit a few turns from the bottom (Figure 3-1). While not the most sophisticated way, this works well for fixed frequency operation where the antenna is cut to length. For example, using the coil outlined above, tuning the air-variable cap to roughly half value, cutting an antenna to 42 feet, and attaching it to the coil just one turn from the bottom, will attaching it to the coil just one turn from the bottom, will result in a set with good reception of HF AM broadcast stations in the 5-6 Mhz band.

the antenna tuner, a second matching method

A second attachment method, which reduces interaction of the antenna and L-C circuit, is to add an antenna matching circuit, also called an antenna tuner. These circuits are often designed with a shunt coil (to ground) and a series capacitor, as shown in Figure 3-2. L1-C1 make up the tuner, and L2-C2 represent L-C the series resonant circuit of the crystal set. Assuming that the antenna is cut to the right length, it will present 50 ohms of resistance to the set. In addition, the output resistance of the matching network will be low. Limiting its resistance maintains the necessary Q, and selectivity, of the L-C circuit. (See design calculations and chapter 7 for details.)

Hence, our slightly more complicated HF set (Figure 3-2) includes an extra inductor and capacitor, used to match the antenna to the L-C circuit. With an antenna cut to resonance, at a multiple of a quarter-wavelength of the desired listening frequency, this set will produce surprising results.

So go ahead, build this set! You'll be amazed at how easily the lowly crystal set pulls in distant stations - again without batteries. And by listening to stations broadcasting in the 3 to 12 Mhz range, you will experience the ups and downs of the ionosphere, hidden by modern sets featuring automatic volume control (AVC).

Table 3-1: Bill of Materials for the HF Set

part	description
L1	0.35 µH coil, optional
C1	2000 pf, optional
L2	3.5 µH air-wound coil: 9 turns #16, 2" dia., 1.5" length
C2	365 pf air variable
D	1N6263 or 1N34 diode (or galena and cat whisker!)
C3	1000 pf
P	4000 ohm (or 2000) headphones

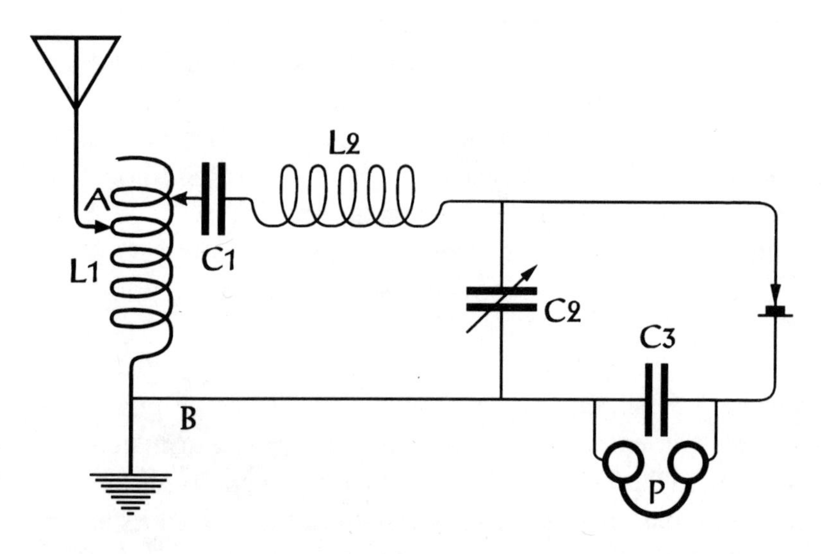

Figure 3-2: An HF crystal set

calculations for an HF crystal set

For the math minded, constants, formulas, and calculations for the HF crystal set are shown below. The calculations were performed using MATHCAD on a PC. Theory supporting these calculations can be found in chapters 7 and 8.

Start with wide bandwidth (moderate selectivity). Frequency (f) = 5.85 Mhz, band width (BW) = 180 Khz.

$$f = 5.85 \cdot 10^6 \quad BW = 180 \cdot 10^3$$

$$Q = \frac{f}{BW} \qquad Q = 32.5$$

Given L-C coil of 3.5 μH, capacitance (C) = 211 picofarads (pf). w = radian frequency in Hz, XL = reactance in ohms.

$$w = 2\pi \cdot f \quad L = 3.5 \cdot 10^{-6}$$

$$XL = w \cdot L \quad C = \frac{1}{w^2 \cdot L} \quad C = 2.115 \cdot 10^{-10}$$

The equivalent parallel resistance (R_p) of the L-C circuit at resonance is 4 Kohms.

$$XL = 128.648 \quad R_p = XL \cdot Q \quad R_p = 4.181 \cdot 10^3$$

R_{series} is the equivalent series resistance of the L-C coil. We must match this value to the 50 ohms of the antenna.

$$R_{series} = \frac{R_P}{Q^2 + 1} \quad R_{series} = 3.955$$

R_{ant} is the resistance of the antenna; it must be matched to the series resistance of the L-C circuit, R_{series}.

$$R_{ant} = 50 \quad Q2 = \sqrt{\frac{R_{ant} - R_{series}}{R_{series}}} \quad Q2 = 3.412$$

X_P is the inductance in ohms of the coil attached directly from the antenna to ground.

$$X_P = \frac{R_{\text{ant}}}{Q2} \quad X_P = 14.653 \quad X_S = R_{\text{series}} \cdot \frac{R_{\text{ant}}}{X_P}$$

The series equivalent coil is essentially the same value, given Q2>3.

$$X_S = 13.494 \quad L_S = \frac{X_S}{w} \quad L_S = 3.671 \cdot 10^{-7}$$

Hence L_S and C_S, the parts of the matching network are respectively 3.6 μH and 2000 pf (or .002 μfd).

$$C_S = \frac{1}{w^2 \cdot L_S} \quad C_S = 2.016 \cdot 10^{-9}$$

DID INSECTS BEAT US TO RADIO?

Jerome N. Goggin, Claremont, NH

The Insects, a volume of *The Life Nature Library* (Time-Life Books, 1962), contains a remarkable statement, "Some species of moths respond to the attracting scent of a female more than a mile away."

Incredible! If true how is it possible? At so great a distance the scent would seem immeasurably dilute. And molecules of the scent, which is chemically known as a pheromone, are typically 5 to 10 times heavier than molecules of oxygen and nitrogen in air and would probably sink to the ground before blown that far by the wind. And, if random molecules of the pheromone did contact the male, would their concentration be great enough for him to detect the direction of their source? Add to this the fact that male moths have been observed flying toward the scent even though they were upwind from it, and we have the makings of a fascinating entomological mystery!

One observer who reflected on this phenomenon was a famous French entomologist, Jean Henri Fabre, who studied the great peacock moth. In a paper published in 1905 he wrote:

"Physical science is today preparing to give us wireless telegraphy by means of Hertzian waves. Can the Great Peacock Moth have anticipated our efforts in this direction? ...can the newly hatched bride have at her disposal electric or magnetic waves, which one sort of screen would arrest and another let through?"

A very exciting question, is it not?

A more modern researcher, Dr. Philip S. Callahan (Ph.D. Kansas State University) elaborates on this theme in a book entitled, *Insect Behavior* (1970). Dr. Callahan raises the question: "Do insects utilize certain wavelengths to maintain communication with one another?"

After describing some tantalizing examples observed in nature, Dr. Callahan writes, "My theory was that the scent itself is an electromagnetic transmitter and the moth antennae detect, or couple to, the electromagnetic energy from the free floating scent molecules.... We know that the vibrational motion of molecules generates infrared absorption bands. These bands are specific IR frequencies; their wavelengths depend on the configuration of the molecule. The end-over-end rotations of an entire molecule results in microwave frequency generation.... A scent molecule might be considered a small satellite, transmitting microwave and infrared frequencies.... If any one species of male moths had antennae that were 'tuned' to IR or microwave frequencies of the vibrating scent molecules given off by the female, the male would 'home in' toward the approaching molecule because that would be the direction of highest signal strength."

Elsewhere he states, "It might be a combination of frequencies...that trigger the antennal response, with different spines and lengths of spines being tuned for different frequencies that together give a coded signal. Antennal spines on moths occur in graduated lengths and various arrays, just as with certain radio and TV antennae arrangements."

Dr. Callahan continues, "I have been able to demonstrate in my laboratory that certain spines, called 'sensillae' on moths are capable of receiving electromagnetic energy. The cecropia moth antennae have some very fine-pointed sensillae at the most basal portion of the antennae. I mounted a live moth under a dissecting scope and connected an amplifier to the central antenna nerve. When I radiated these spines with either visible light from a microscope lamp or a low-power red laser beam and chopped the beam with a revolving fan blade, I picked up the chopped signal from the antenna nerve on my oscilloscope. The laser light, which is like radio in that it is coherent (all waves traveling in unison), was the most efficient. This is the first report of an insect antenna spine responding to pure electromagnetic frequency."

So, do bugs have radio or not? Dr. Callahan cautions, "The infrared and microwave spectrum is so vast...that much work lies ahead before anyone can be certain my theories are entirely correct."

On the other hand, is it really so far-fetched to think that insects may tune to parts of the electromagnetic spectrum other than the narrow band humans call "light"? I know I shall never again experience a summer evening without bemused speculation about another, hidden world coexisting with my own. And I shall wish for a radio to eavesdrop on its inhabitants. For I believe the broadcast bands of the alien races will teem with transmissions, as multitudes of otherwise silent, unseen beings signal frantically to others of their kind, "Here I am; I am your species!"

TIDBITS....

Larry Hall, Morgan, Utah, sent us a note about his brass Morse Decoder coin. One side features the letters of the alphabet, and the other side has a dot-dash tree that ends appropriately with each letter displayed. Any interest? Larry also sent us a nice note stating, "I enjoyed building your toroidal crystal set. When finished, I couldn't resist mounting it in a small match box." From the photo sent it appears that he glued a knob onto the compression capacitor to allow easy tuning.

MEMBERSHIP CORRESPONDENCE

Bill Cline, who recently purchased Volume One of the newsletter, sent us a note about a fox-hole radio. "When I was in grade school I recall that a fellow student brought a fox-hole radio to school. It used a blue razor blade as the diode, and we were told that it was used in WW-II." Bill also mentions that he found an article about this in *Popular Mechanics*, but he couldn't recall the exact issue, perhaps October of 1962 or 1963. If anyone locates the article let us know.

R. I. Leister, N3KAS, Pottstown, PA, writes, "I run JAMBOREE ON THE AIR (JOTA) for my local Boy Scout Council each year. This time I wanted to add some memories for the Scouts with graying temples - i.e. a crystal set demo. I constructed the Quaker Oats variety from memory with a pyrite crystal and cat whisker which worked the first try! I also built your version (with 1N34 diode) from the February [1993] issue of Nuts & Volts. Both were a hit! What surprised me was that the 7-12 year olds were intrigued too. After visiting hours at our cabin, everyone listened to the World Series on both sets."

James Hayward, Mississauga, Ontario, Canada sent us a note stating how much he has enjoyed reading his copies of Volumes I and II of the newsletter. He also enclosed some notes on a portable crystal set he has designed and built. Portable means just that, you carry it around with you - no permanent antenna hung in a tree. His set is about one meter long and uses several flat ferrite bars stacked end-to-end! He's prepared to tell us more if there's interest!

VENDORS

Someone wrote me last month inquiring about Rainy Day Books. At the time I couldn't find my reference file so I went to press with issue #14 without it. While cleaning my study today I found a postcard dated 4/8/93 from Jerome Goggin, listing the address: **Rainy Day Books**, P.O. Box 775, Fitzwilliam, NH, 03447. Thanks (again!) Jerome.

QSL Card

Do you want to send QSL cards to AM or HF stations confirming reception? If so we've included a design shown below for your use.

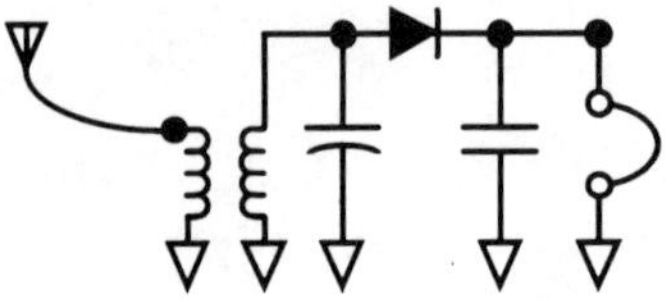

Member: The Xtal Set Society

Name

Street

City State

County

Confirming Reception of	Date Day	Month	Year	UTC	Mhz	RST	Mode

Reception PSE QSL

CHAPTER 4

COIL INDUCTANCE FORMULAS

This chapter presents a number of convenient formulas for calculating coil inductance. Coils play a part in every crystal set, and their design and construction is, perhaps, the most enjoyable task in building a set. Coils are used to tune the antenna to resonance, couple the antenna to the set, tune the set, filter out unwanted signals, and couple the set to the detector and headphones. In basic sets - those without a tuning capacitor - the coil is the sole tuning element.

Experimenters over the years have found a number of ingenious forms on which to wind their coils: pieces of wood, match boxes, cardboard cut-out patterns, toilet paper roles, pieces of PVC pipe, Quaker Oats boxes, and more! Figure 4-1 depicts three popular forms: rectangular, cylindrical, and spider-web. Experimenters in the 20s often wound their coils on pieces of wood or match boxes. Wire at that time was cotton covered (WCC) to prevent shorting between turns. Figure 4-1a shows a typical coil. The wire can be closely wound, each turn touching the next, or the turns can be spaced out. Figure 4-1b displays today's usual choice, the cylindrical coil. PVC pipe pieces or an oats box are convenient forms. Figure 4-1c shows the spider-web arrangement. The form can be fashioned from heavy cardboard or plywood. The arrangement was adopted by early experimenters to reduce the capacitance between wires, thereby allowing for more coil inductance at a given frequency. Coil capacitance is covered in chapter 5.

Coil design is an important factor for crystal set performance. The inductance of the coil must match that required for the set, and the heat losses in the coil,

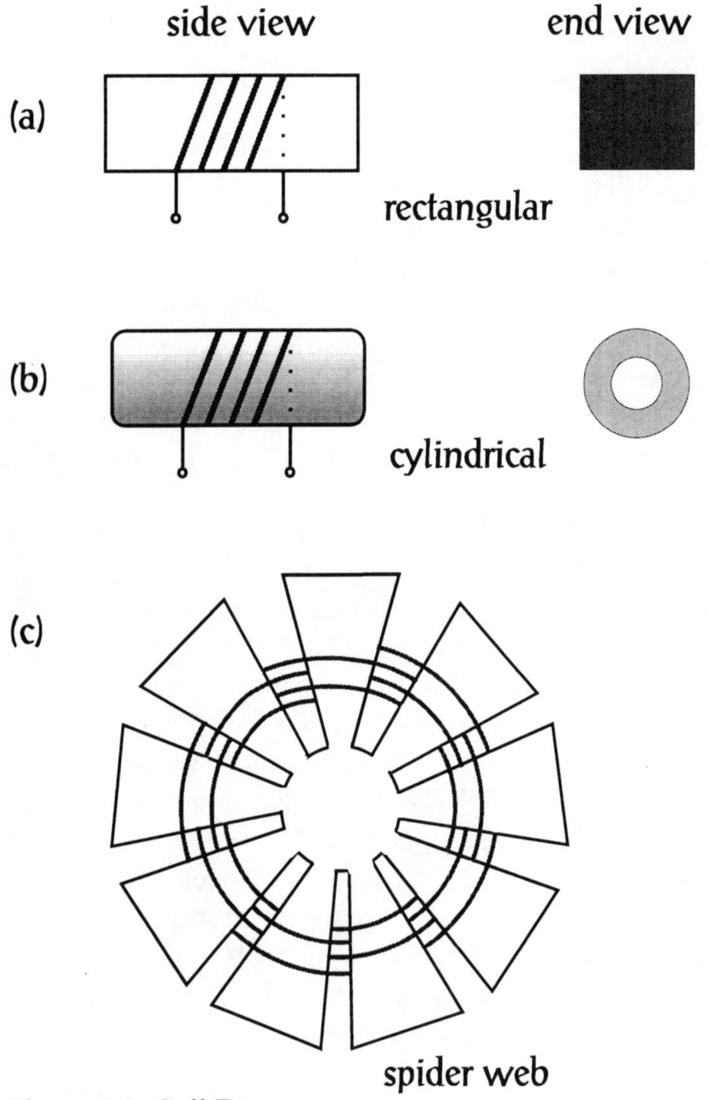

Figure 4-1: Coil Forms

characterized by the Q of the coil, must be kept to a minimum, particularly for HF sets. Inductance must be maximized too when maximum signal reception is desired. Hence, coil capacitance must be minimized. Fortunately, coil inductance and coil Q, for a given coil design, can be calculated, and capacitance can be measured.

Coil Formulas

This section contains formulas for calculating the inductance of single-layer coils; basket-weave, spider-web, and multi-layer coils are not included. Because many early crystal sets utilized coil forms with a square or rectangular end shape, an inductance formula for general cross-sections is presented first. To this we add several formulas using a cylindrical form. Formula 4-4 is probably the most popular, expressing inductance in terms of number of turns and coil diameter and coil length in inches.

Rule of thumb. As the formulas listed below will illustrate, the inductance of a coil is proportional to the square of the number of turns if the dimensions are held constant. Also, if the turns are held constant the inductance is proportional to the cross-sectional area and inversely proportional to the length of the coil.

Single-layer coil, any cross-section
(dimensions in meters)

The formula for a single-layer coil of any cross-sectional design is shown below.

$$L = \frac{(\mu \cdot N^2 \cdot A)}{\text{length}} \qquad \text{Formula 4-1}$$

where:
L = inductance in Henrys
$\mu = 12.56 \cdot 10^{-7}$, for air (permeability)
N = number of turns of the coil
A = cross-sectional area in square meters
length = length of the coil in meters

The cross sectional area need not be circular or square; it can be any shape. The formula is not accurate for coils whose length:area (ratio) is small. For length:area equal to 4, calculated inductance can be off by as much as 10%. For length:area equal to 10, error is <4%. The error is due to end effects.

Formula 4-1 is most useful if arranged for inches.

$$L = \frac{49.45 \cdot N^2 \cdot A}{\text{length}} \qquad \text{Formula 4-1b, inches.}$$

where:
L = inductance in microhenry
N = number of wire turns
A = area in square inches
length = coil length in inches

<u>Short coils, circular cross-section</u>
(dimensions in meters)

An accurate formula for cylindrical coils is shown below.

$$L = \frac{(\mu \cdot N^2 \cdot A)}{(\text{length} + 0.45 \cdot \text{diameter})} \qquad \text{Formula 4-2}$$

where:
L = inductance in Henrys
μ, N, A, and length are as defined in (1)
diameter = diameter of the cylinder in meters

This formula is accurate within 1% if the length:diameter (ratio) is greater than 0.4.

Coils with circular cross-section

This formula is similar to the one above but is in, perhaps, a more practical form; dimensions are in inches.

$$L = \frac{(r^2 \cdot N^2)}{(10 \cdot \text{length} + 9 \cdot r)} \qquad \text{Formula 4-3}$$

where:
L = inductance in microhenrys
r = radius of the coil in inches
N = number of turns on the coil
length = length of the coil in inches

It is assumed, of course, that the wire, the form, and everything in the immediate vicinity of the coil is nonmagnetic. This formula is accurate within 1% if the length:r (ratio) is > 0.5.

The formula can also be expressed in terms of the diameter, which may be convenient. This is the 'so-called' low frequency inductance formula.

$$L = \frac{\left(d^2 \cdot N^2\right)}{\left[\left(18 \cdot d\right) + \left(40 \cdot \text{length}\right)\right]}$$ Formula 4-4

where:
L = inductance in microhenrys,
N = number of turns on the coil,
d = diameter in inches, and
r = radius in inches.
length=length of coil in inches

CHAPTER 5

Coil 'Q' and coil capacitance

This chapter presents a formula for estimating the coil quality factor 'Q' and a procedure for measuring coil capacitance. These characteristics are important because they affect crystal set selectivity (bandwidth) and sensitivity (attainable volume).

Selectivity is a measure of how well a set or L-C circuit separates stations we may hear that broadcast on frequencies near one another. We might say a set is highly selective if it does a good job of separating these signals. Selectivity can also be defined in terms of L-C circuit bandwidth. Bandwidth is defined as the frequency band over which the circuit maintains a response of at least half that at its maximum. This is also referred to as the half-power bandwidth. For example, if a set produces a signal (power received) of at least one half that heard at 1000 Khz from 900 to 1100 Khz, then the bandwidth is said to be 200 Khz.

Hence, the bandwidth defines the quality factor or Q of an L-C circuit. We simply define the Q to be the ratio of the tuned circuit's peak frequency to its bandwidth. As a result, the narrower the bandwidth, the higher the Q and selectivity. In formula form, Q is denoted as follows:

$$Q = \frac{f_O}{BW} \qquad \text{Formula 5-1}$$

where:
BW is the bandwidth of a single-tuned circuit set
f_0 is the peak listening frequency
Q is the loaded Q of the circuit.

The loaded Q of a tuned circuit (the Q of the set as a whole) is determined by loading from the antenna, the detector with headphones, and the Q of the coil itself. To optimize selectivity and received signal strength, the Q of the coil itself must be high. If loading by the antenna and detector is 'light,' the Q of the coil itself - called the unloaded Q - sets the crystal set Q.

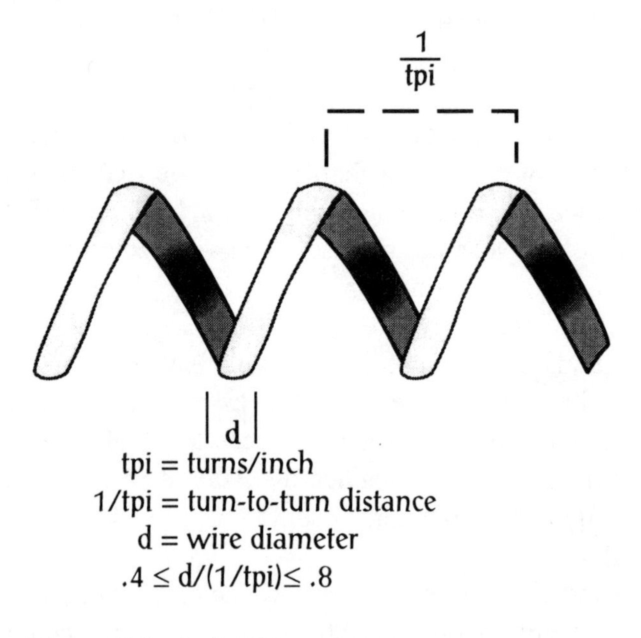

Figure 5-1: Coil Q Restrictions

Measuring coil Q takes specialized equipment, and it is hard to obtain accurate results with homebrew test equipment. For this reason, it's best to estimate coil Q by formula. With some restrictions listed below and noted in Figure 5-1, the following formula may be used.

$$Q = CF \cdot d \cdot \sqrt{f} \qquad \text{Formula 5-2}$$

where:
CF = correction factor
d = coil diameter in inches
f = frequency in Mhz

The formula is valid if solid copper wire is used and if the wire diameter:turn-to-turn distance ratio lies between about .4 and .8 (Figure 5-1). Given that these restrictions are met, the correction factor (CF) is determined by the length:diameter of the coil. For example, using the table below, a coil with a length:diameter ratio of 1 would have a correction factor of 100.

TABLE (5-1): Q correction factors given coil length:diameter ratio

CF	length:diameter
135	4.0
120	2.0
100	1.0
80	.50
60	.25

As an example, let's calculate the Q of a coil as specified below:

#20 wire (32 mils diameter, 26 turns/inch)
16 turns/inch when wound
frequency of operation = 1 Megahertz
coil diameter = 2 inches
coil length = 1 inch.

To make sure the formula applies, let's check the wire diameter : turn-to-turn distance first. The ratio is $\frac{.032}{1/16}$ or .51 which is within proper range. The estimated Q of the coil is then 160.

$$Q = 80 \cdot 2 \cdot \sqrt{1} = 160$$

Rule of Thumb. Note that if the dimensions of the coil are held constant, the Q increases as the square root of the frequency.

Coil Capacitance

Self-capacitance of coils is unimportant at low frequencies, but becomes a factor for high frequency crystal sets. At some frequency, the coil will be self-resonant; its inductance will form a parallel tuned circuit with its capacitance. When this happens the coil is no longer useful as an inductor!

A coil designed to be an inductance will necessarily have some capacitance distributed along the wire. There is capacitance between every inch of wire and every other inch, and between each inch of wire and ground. The amount of distributed capacitance depends on the construction of the coil; it is highest if the coil is wound in layers with turns from opposite ends of the wire lying on top of each other. Coils used for radio circuits are ordinarily designed to reduce self-capacitance. It is nearly impossible to calculate the self-capacitance of a coil but it can be readily measured.

Rule of Thumb. It proves to be a good approximation to represent the total capacitance of the coil as one capacitor across the coil leads.

To demonstrate coil capacitance, a coil was wound on a Quaker Oats box and its capacitance was measured each time five turns of wire were added. These data are listed in Table 5-2.

TABLE 5-2: Capacitance of a 5 Inch Coil

turns	self-resonant frequency (Mhz)	capacitance (pf)	inductance (μH)
10	10.3	10	21
15	6.5	14	44
20	4.7	16	72
25	3.4	24	102

The coil was constructed using #22 wire, 15 turns:inch (tpi). An IFR radio-frequency signal generator was used to introduce the test signal into the coil, tapped at three turns from the bottom. An oscilloscope with a ten μμfd (pf) capacitance probe was attached to the coil at the turns indicated. Measurements were taken after each batch of five turns was added to the coil. As expected the resonant frequency went down as turns were added. The capacitance figures were calculated after figuring the inductance, using one of the coil formulas listed in chapter 4. The capacitance listed in the table includes that of the scope probe.

What's this all mean? On the practical side, the coil is useful as an inductor only at frequencies well below self-resonance. As self-capacitance is allowed to build up, available coil inductance (for a given frequency of operation) is reduced. This can affect set volume, selectivity, and filtering capabilities.

Rule of Thumb. For best selectivity and high loaded circuit Q, keep the coil capacitance low.

Measuring Coil Capacitance

The data in Table 5-2 shows the presence of self-capacitance for the coils constructed. However, the method used to obtain an estimate of the capacitance can be improved upon. We need a procedure that will allow us to make just a couple of measurements on a coil and calculate its capacitance directly. An simple equipment arrangement to do this is shown in Figure 5-2, and measurement steps are outlined below.

To measure coil capacitance, you'll need a signal generator, a variable capacitor, and a scope or detector circuit and volt-ohm meter (VOM). The capacitor needs to have a calibrated dial. If the signal generator has good drive, a detector and VOM can be used to measure resonant peaks instead of the scope. If you try this method, we suggest a germanium diode, a 47K resistor and .001 μfd cap as the detector.

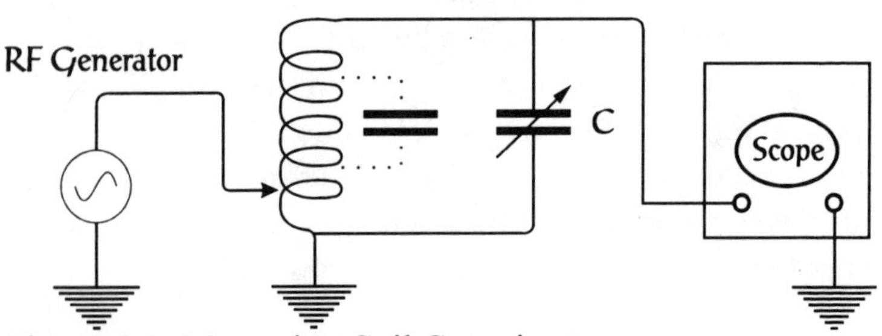

Figure 5-2: Measuring Coil Capacitance

In order to obtain the coil capacitance you'll have to make two measurements: one at a frequency somewhat below coil self-resonance, and one at half that frequency. With the coil in parallel with the tuning cap, with the generator tapped a few turns from the bottom of the coil, and with the scope probe or detector attached to the top of the coil, follow the procedures outlined below.

1. Peak the displayed signal after setting the generator to the first frequency - say 1/2 of the self resonant frequency - by varying the tuning capacitor. Note the capacitor value (which we'll call C1).

2. Reduce the generator frequency to half that just used and again vary the tuning capacitor until the scope or detector peaks. Note the cap value again (C2).

3. Then calculate the self-capacitance of the coil using the following formula.

$$C_0 = \frac{\left[C2 - (4 \cdot C1)\right]}{3} \quad \text{Formula 5-3}$$

where:
C_0 = self-capacitance, (same units as C2 and C1)
C1 = tuning capacitor value at frequency 1
C2 = cap value at frequency 2 half of f1

Formula Derivations: Coil Capacitance, True Inductance, and True Q

If you're like me, you'll want to see a proof of formula 5-3, and you might wonder if true coil Q or inductance is increased or decreased by the coil capacitance. If you don't care about a proof for formula 5-3, skip to the next chapter.

A derivation of formula 5-3 is outlined below, and, yes, true coil Q and inductance are affected by coil capacitance. If you disregard the coil capacitance and depend upon the external capacitance alone (C in Figure 5-2) to calculate/determine L, your answer will be off.

$$L_{\text{true}}\,(\text{true inductance}) = \frac{L_{\text{measured}} \cdot C}{C + C_O} \quad \text{and}$$

$$Q_{\text{true}}\left(\text{true } Q\right) = \frac{Q_{\text{measured}} \cdot \left(C + C_O\right)}{C}$$

derivation of coil capacitance formula

Let's start by examining Figure 5-2. Previously, we discussed taking measurements at two frequencies below coil self-resonance, one at f1, and one at f2 or half the frequency of f1. Given the general formula for the frequency of a resonance L-C circuit, Formula 5-4, it is clear that the capacitance at f2 must be four times that at f1 (assuming we don't change the coil).

$$f = \frac{1}{2\pi} \cdot \frac{1}{\sqrt{LC_{\text{total}}}} \qquad \text{Formula 5-4}$$

where:
$C_{total} = C_O + C$
C_O = coil capacitance
C = external measurement capacitor.

Hence, C_{total} at f2 is four times C_{total} at f1, or

$$C1 + C_0 = \frac{C2 + C_0}{4}.$$

It follows then that

$$C_O = \frac{C_2 - \left(4 \cdot C_1\right)}{3}$$

where:
C_1 = external capacitance measured at f1
C_2 = external capacitance measured at f2
f1 = twice f2

derivation of equations for L_{true}, Q_{true}

If you use equipment as shown in Figure 5-2 to determine coil inductance directly - peak with C and calculate L - the value will be off as mentioned above. To determine a correction factor when using the equipment, start with formula 5-4, but invert and square both sides.

$$\frac{1}{f^2} = 4\pi^2 \cdot L \cdot (C + C_0) \qquad \text{Formula 5-5}$$

The $1/f^2$ equation for true inductance includes C_0, but for measured inductance it does not. Hence an inductance ratio can be expressed as

$$\frac{L_{\text{true}}}{L_{\text{measured}}} = \frac{\dfrac{1}{4\pi^2 \cdot L(C + C_0)}}{\dfrac{1}{4\pi^2 \cdot L \cdot C}} = \frac{C}{C + C_0}$$

Hence,

$$L_{\text{true}} = L_{\text{measured}} \cdot \left(\frac{C}{C + C_0} \right) \qquad \text{Formula 5-6}$$

In like manner, a correction factor for true Q can be determined. Form a ratio of true Q to measured Q using true and measured inductance.

$$\frac{R/L_{\text{true}}}{R/L_{\text{measured}}} = \frac{L_{\text{measured}}}{L_{\text{true}}} = \frac{C + C_0}{C}$$

Hence,

$$\frac{Q_{\text{true}}}{Q_{\text{measured}}} = \left(\frac{C + C_0}{C}\right) \qquad \text{Formula 5-7}$$

In closing, it's interesting to note that formula 5-5 is an equation for a straight line, and takes the form $y = m \cdot x + b$ as shown in Figure 5-3. *m* is the slope of the line, C is the x variable, and b is the y intercept. A bit of algebra will show that true inductance is proportional to the slope.

$$L_{\text{true}} = \frac{m}{4\pi^2}$$

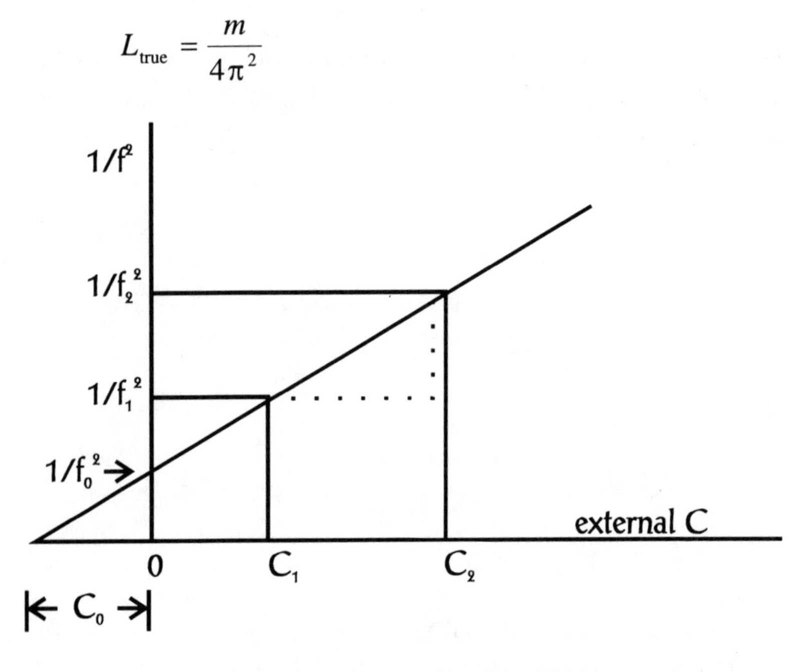

Figure 5-3: Inductance is Proportional to Slope

CHAPTER 6

DETECTOR LOADING

For all crystal sets (that can truly be called crystal sets) some sort of passive AM detector circuit is used. The most common configuration is shown in Figure 6-1, consisting of a detector diode (D), a capacitor (C), and a resistor (P) (the resistance of the headphones). In fact, this circuit is still one of the most widely used demodulators for AM signals; almost every modern day superheterodyne AM receiver has one.

In order to optimize a crystal set for selectivity or volume, it is useful to realize how this basic AM detector *loads* the tuned circuit. The detector, in fact, can be modeled as a resistor. As such, we can substitute the resistor for the detector and easily calculate its effects on the L-C circuit.

Provided that the tuned circuit Q is high enough (>5), there is a neat and simple *rule of thumb* we can use: *The value of the resistor is one-half the headphone resistance.* For example, if you remove the detector and 2,000 ohm headphones and put in their place a 1,000 ohm resistor, you will measure exactly the same voltage at the tuned circuit with an oscilloscope! The bottom of Figure 6-1 illustrates that a resistor can replace the diode and headphones for calculation purposes. Both circuits are identical if the Q of the L-C circuit is high enough, and this is usually true in practice.

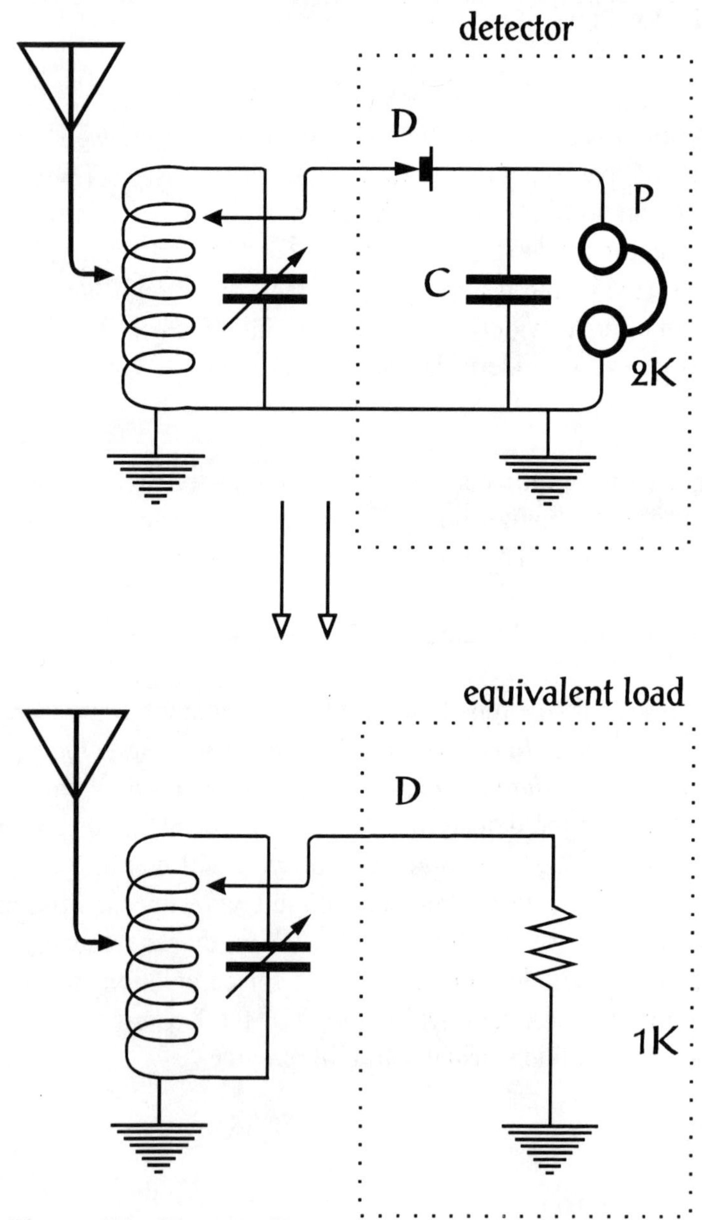

Figure 6-1: Common Detector

Studying figure 6-2 will reveal why this simple rule of thumb is plausible. Assume that a steady RF signal is introduced to the crystal set. The figure shows the DC current developed at the detector, and it displays the current spikes that recharge the capacitor back to a DC voltage level each RF cycle. The RF signal current at the operating frequency has a steady-state amplitude that is twice the DC current. This can be shown to be true by expanding the diode current (the spikes) in a Fourier Series (Clarke, 1978). Hence, the tuned circuit, at the operating frequency, "sees" a load resistance that is one-half that seen by the DC current.

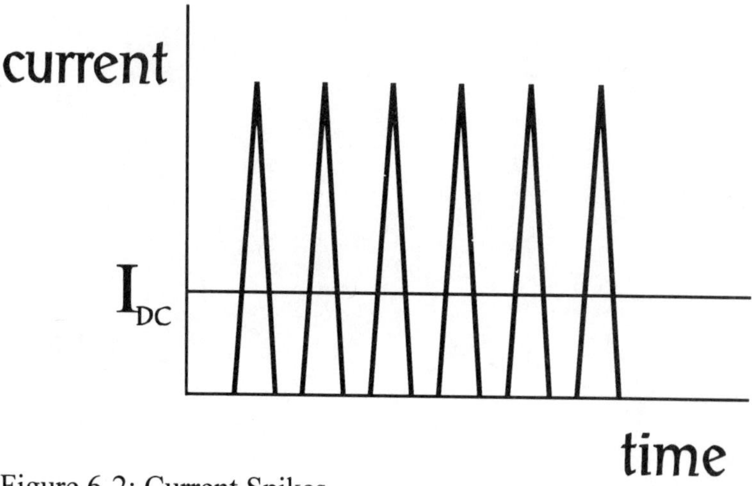

Figure 6-2: Current Spikes

CHAPTER 7

MATCHING ANTENNA AND DETECTOR FOR MAXIMUM CRYSTAL SET VOLUME

If you've experimented with crystal sets, particularly for shortwave listening, you've discovered that it is critical how the antenna and headphones are attached to the set (L-C circuit). By optimizing these connections, you'll insure that maximum audio will be obtained. For engineers and radio techs, to insure maximum volume means the same thing as "to match".

The basis for this process is the maximum power transfer principle. This fundamental rule can be stated as follows:

> Maximum power is transferred from a source to a load when the impedance of the source is matched to the impedance of the load.

Applied to crystal sets, we can state the rule in practical terms:

> Maximum volume is heard in the headphones when the detector and phones are matched to the L-C circuit and the circuit, in turn, is matched to the antenna.

Following this rule will produce maximum volume but not necessarily good selectivity. Matching for selectivity is discussed in the next chapter on advanced matching.

The maximum power transfer principle applies equally to DC, audio, radio frequency communication circuits, and even mechanical systems. Our interest, of course, is in how it applies to radio communication circuits. We need to match the impedance of the antenna to the set and the set to the headphones. If we do that, we insure the maximum transfer of available signal power from the antenna for listening. That's our goal!

Matching of RF communication circuits can take many forms, using coils or caps (or a combination of both), broadband transformers, and transistor circuits. The simplest matching method uses a coil and cap to match a low resistance to a high resistance or a high resistance to a low resistance. For example, we might want to match the low resistance and capacitance of an end-fed wire antenna to the high resistance of a high Q L-C circuit. Or, we might want to match the high parallel resistance of that high Q circuit to the lower resistance of a detector diode and headphones.

matching secret

As it turns out, nature is kind to us again! A little known fact about series and parallel R-L or R-C circuits is the key to most communications circuit matching. Here's the secret:

> At one frequency (just one frequency), a series R-L circuit has an equivalent parallel R-L circuit; that is, you can't tell them apart if they're placed inside a box! The same is true for a pair of R-C circuits.

This AC circuit secret is shown in Figure 7-1; the circuit on the right, at one frequency, is equivalent to the circuit on the left. If you apply an RF generator to either circuit, the resulting current will be exactly the same - in amplitude and phase. A proof of this phenomenon is presented at the end of this chapter.

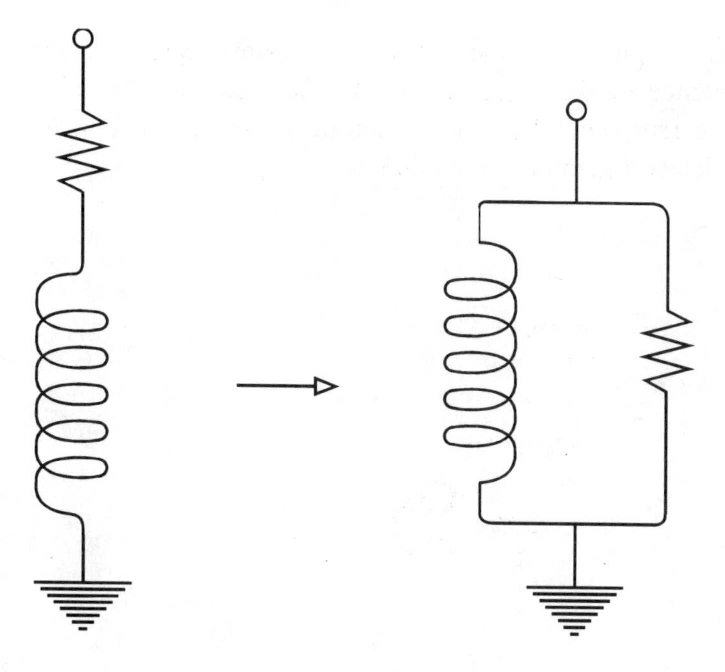

Figure 7-1: R-L Circuit

matching applied to the simplest crystal set

Perhaps the best way to see how our power rule and circuit secret can apply to RF communication circuits is to demonstrate their use with the simplest of crystal sets, shown in Figure 7-2. For our example — to keep it simple — let's assume the antenna has a resistance of 50 ohms at the frequency of reception. The remainder of the set consists of an antenna coil, diode, and headphones. To match the set, we're going to add a capacitor.

Before we do that, however, let's redo the schematic. The equivalent electronic circuit of the set is shown at the bottom of 7-2a. The circle with the sine wave inside represents the antenna signal and the 50 ohm resistor represents the impedance of the antenna. On the far right, the 1K ohm resistor represents the detector and headphones (see Chapter 6 on detector loading for details).

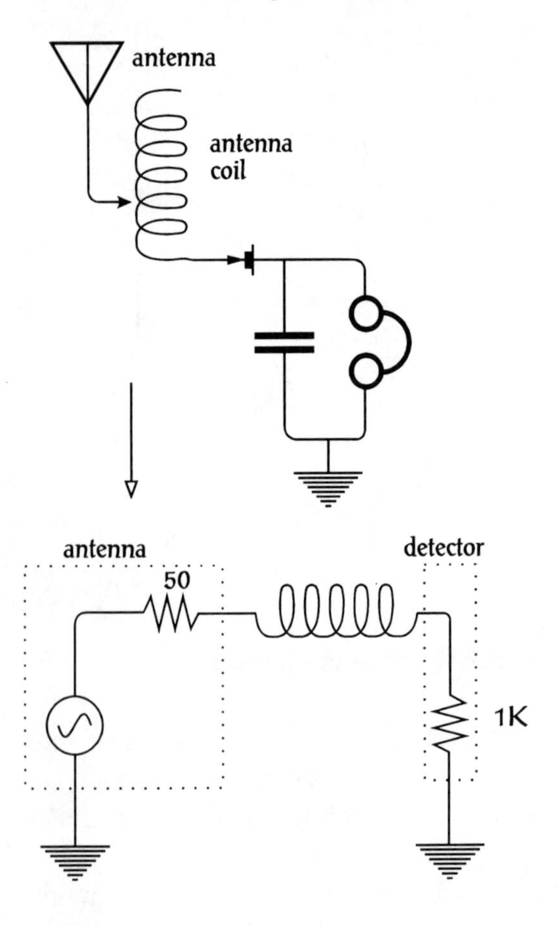

Figure 7-2(a): Matching

Now, as shown at the top of 7-2b, let's add the capacitor, C. By placing it in parallel with the 1K resistor (detector equivalent), we'll effectively decrease the value of the resistor (a proof of this is shown later). Hence, with C in place, L and C together form our matching circuit. At this point, we can apply our R-C secret: we replace the 1K resistor and C with two components in series, R' and C' at the frequency of reception. The result is shown at the bottom of 7-2b. The reactance of C' will be about the same as C (assuming circuit Q is >10), but the series resistor, R', will decrease in value.

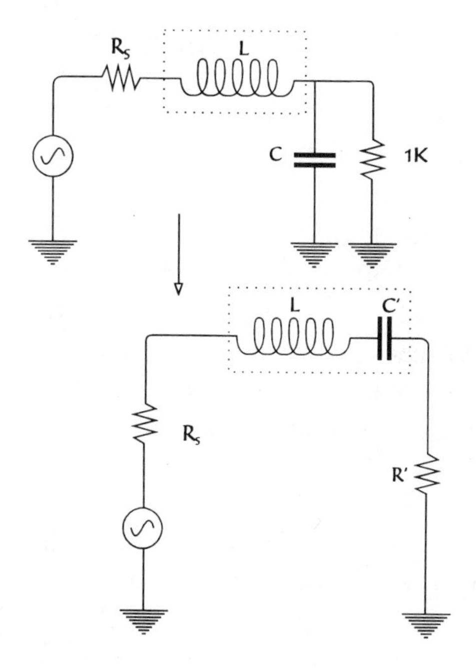

Figure 7-2(b): Matching

The resulting series L-C' combination forms a resonant circuit; hence its impedance at the reception frequency is zero. So, the impedance of the whole circuit (R_S-L-C'-R') is essentially just the new resistor R' that is in series with the antenna impedance of equal value, as shown in Figure 7-2(c).

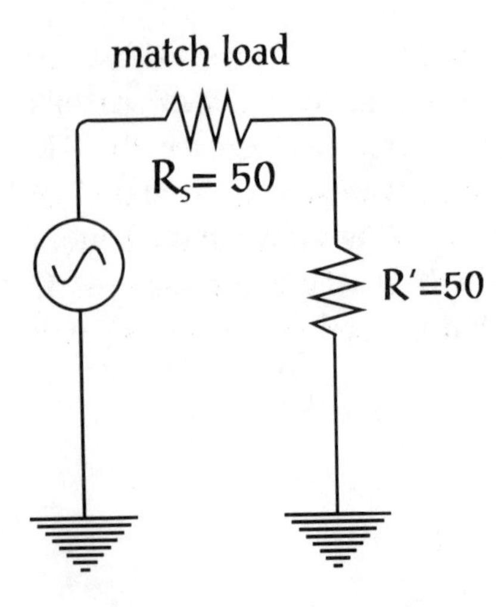

Figure 7-2(c): Matching

In summary, impedances in RF circuits are often matched by adding a coil, a capacitor, or both in a circuit at a critical point. In our example the coil was already a part of the circuit; hence, we added a capacitor to 'resonate out' the coil inductance and decrease the load resistance. The resistors remaining - given that L and C are properly selected - match each other!

Please keep in mind that the actual circuit is that shown at the top of 7-2a. Nobody took away the antenna coil, detector, or matching capacitor. However, we've selected their values so that L and C effectively disappear and the detector resistance is made to appear equal to the antenna resistance. By matching these resistors we insure maximum crystal set volume.

If you are an antenna expert, no doubt you noticed our 50 ohm antenna in the example was optimistically simplified — to make the example simple. It is true, however, that an end-feed antenna which is less than a quarter wave length will have some capacitance too. This doesn't really change our example though since the reactance of the antenna capacitance simply reduces the value of the coil reactance a small amount.

formulas, examples, derivations

Two formulas allow us to calculate parallel or series equivalents for R-L or R-C circuits. The following pair are arranged to calculate parallel equivalents to a series set:

$$R_P = R_S \cdot \left(Q^2 + 1\right) \text{ and } X_P = {R_P}/{Q}$$

where R_p is the parallel resistance
R_s is the series resistance
Q is the Q of the coil
X_p is the reactance of the parallel coil or cap
X_s is the reactance of the series coil or cap
Q is the series or parallel Q of the circuit where

$$Q_P = Q_S \text{ and } Q_S = {X_S}/{R_S} \quad Q_P = {R_P}/{X_P}$$

We can use algebra to rearrange these formulas for series equivalent calculations. A derivation of these formulas is presented at the end of this chapter.

At this point, let's do some examples. Let's start by converting a 1 ohm resistor and 10 ohm (reactance) coil in series into their parallel equivalent set.

$$R_S = 1 \quad X_S = 10 \quad Q_S = \frac{X_s}{R_S} \quad Q = Q_S \quad Q = 10$$

$$R_P = R_S\left(Q^2 + 1\right) \quad R_P = 101 \quad \mathrm{X_P} = \frac{R_P}{Q} \quad \mathrm{X_P} = 10.1$$

Note that the reactance of the parallel coil is nearly the same as its series cousin. In contrast, however, the value of the parallel resistor has exploded in value; it's one hundred times the series resistor! As you can see from the formulas, this is due to the squaring of the coil Q.

For another example let's pick the resistor to be 5 ohms and the coil reactance 10 ohms. Again, we start by calculating the Q. It's smaller this time since the series resistor is bigger. Still, the resistance is boosted and the reactance is only slightly increased.

$$R_S = 5 \quad X_S = 10 \quad Q = \frac{X_S}{R_S} \quad \mathrm{Q} = 2$$

$$R_P = R_S\left(Q^2 + 1\right) \quad R_P = 25 \quad X_P = \frac{R_P}{Q} \quad X_P = 12.5$$

For the math minded, we have outlined below a derivation of the formulas for converting a coil and resistor in series to a coil and resistor in parallel at one frequency. You'll need a background in complex algebra and AC circuits to trace through the equations. We start by equating the admittance of the series circuit to the inverse of its impedance. Using complex algebra, the real and imaginary parts of these equivalents are separated, resulting in formulas for the conductance, G, and susceptance, B. The conductance and susceptance are each inverted, resulting in formulas for the parallel equivalents. These formulas are simplified by substituting Q for reactance:resistor (ratios). More detail on this can be found in the ARRL Handbook.

$$Z = R_S + j \cdot X_S \quad Y = G + j \cdot B \quad Y = \frac{1}{Z}$$

so,

$$G + jB = \frac{1}{R_S + j \cdot X_S}$$

separating real and imaginary parts, we gain G and B,

$$G = \frac{R_S}{R_S^2 + X_S^2} \quad B = \frac{X_S}{R_S^2 + X_S^2}$$

invert G and B to solve for parallel resistance, Rp, and parallel reactance X_P, but X/R=series Q, or simply the circuit Q , hence Rp is,

$$R_P = \frac{1}{G} \quad R_P = \frac{R_S^2 + X_S^2}{R_S} \quad R_P = R_S\left(1 + \frac{X_S^2}{R_S^2}\right)$$

$$R_P = R_S\left(Q^2 + 1\right)$$

invert B to solve for parallel Xp.

$$X_P = \frac{1}{B} \quad X_P = \frac{R_S^2 + X_S^2}{X_S} \quad X_P = X_S\left(1 + \frac{R_S^2}{X_S^2}\right)$$

but, $X_S = \frac{R_S}{Q}$ so,

$$X_P = \frac{R_S\left(1 + Q_S^2\right)}{Q_S} \text{ or } X_P = \frac{R_P}{Q}$$

CHAPTER 8

ADVANCED MATCHING

Matching a low resistance to a high resistance or vice-versa is straightforward; you add series or parallel combinations of coils and caps, as presented in the last chapter. Matching a source and load to a circuit while preserving selectivity (circuit Q), however, generally requires multiple circuits.

The HF crystal set with a single tuned circuit is a perfect example of this; the L-C tuned circuit must retain a high Q to preserve selectivity. Yet, this circuit must be matched to a low antenna impedance and to a low detector resistance. At the frequency of reception, also the resonant frequency of the set, the L-C tuned circuit will appear resistive. The resistance will either be very high or very low, depending upon how it's wired, in parallel or in series. In either case, the impedance of the L-C circuit will be much higher or much lower than the antenna and detector impedances. Hence, we must provide a match to the L-C circuit at the antenna and at the detector.

design outline for an HF crystal set

A straightforward design approach is to divide our problem into three steps:

1. Determine resistance of the L-C circuit to meet bandwidth requirements

2. Design a detector and headphones to L-C circuit match

3. Match the antenna to the resulting L-C circuit

Figure 8-1 depicts this process. To determine the resistance of the R-L-C circuit, we must start (a) by determining the circuit Q, set by the desired bandwidth and reception frequency. Hence, we start by choosing a bandwidth, say 50 Khz.

$$Q = \frac{\text{reception frequency}}{\text{desired bandwidth}}$$

With the desired Q in hand, the required resistance of the high Q L-C circuit can be determined.

$$R_P = Q \cdot \text{coil reactance}$$

The equation is simply a rearrangement of the Q formula for a parallel L-C circuit.

Second (8-1b), let's match the detector and headphones to the resistance of the L-C tuned circuit. The detector and headphones - often called the load - can be represented by a resistor that is half the value of the headphone resistance (see Chapter 6 on detector loading). This resistor equivalent is tapped part way down the coil; this enables us to match its low resistance to the high resistance of the L-C circuit. If selectivity is chosen to be high, Q will be high, and the L-C resistance will be very high, certainly higher than the load. The tap - called an auto-transformer tap - has the same "transformer action" as an inductively coupled transformer. Hence, the ratio of the coil turns to the number of turns of the tap to ground sets the turns ratio, N. The equivalent resistance presented to the L-C circuit is then equal to the square of N times the load resistance.

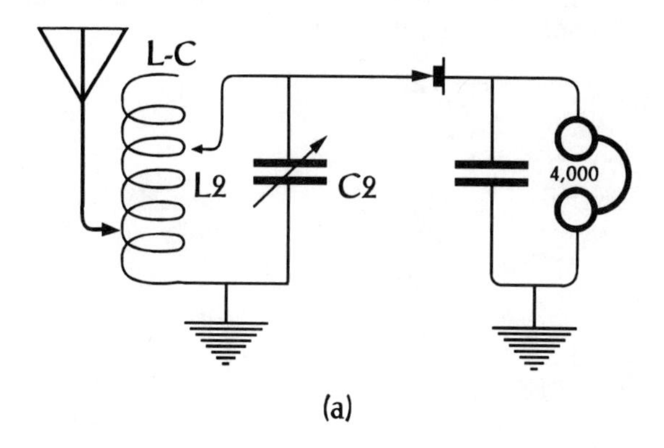

equivalent load

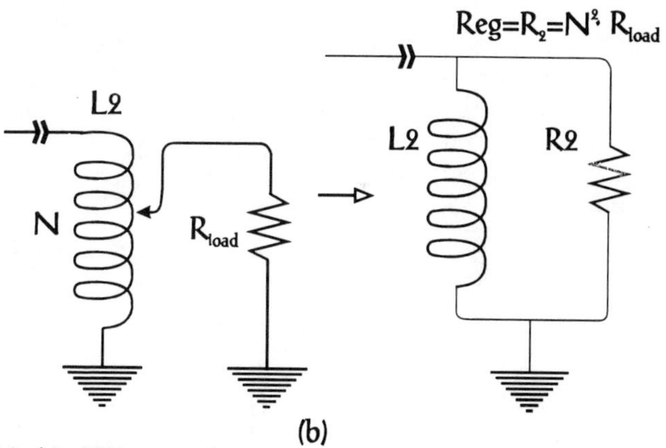

Figure 8-1(a,b): HF crystal set

$$R_{\text{equivalent}} = N^2 \cdot R_{\text{load}}$$

This resistance, of course, must match the required resistance of the L-C circuit. Or,

$$R_P = R_2 = N^2 \cdot R_{\text{load}}$$

So, simply plug in the resistor values needed and solve for N. The tap position is then determined, and our load match design is complete.

$$N = \sqrt{\frac{R_P}{R_{\text{load}}}}$$

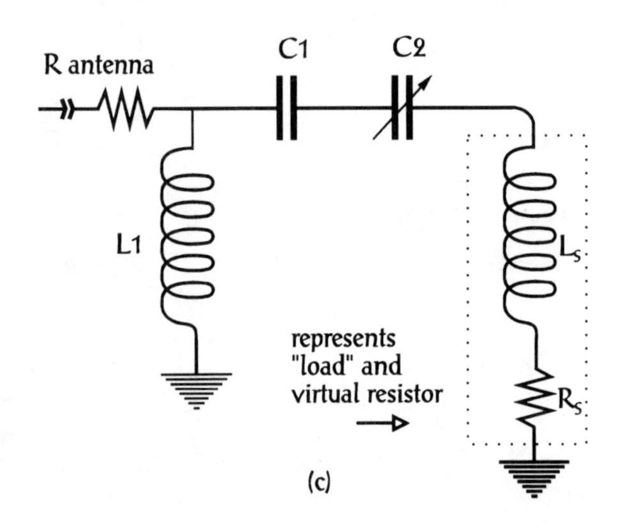

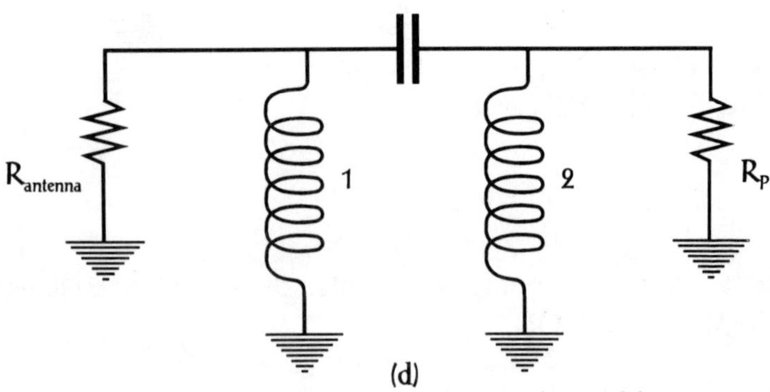

Figure 8-1(c,d): HF crystal set advanced matching

Next (8-1c), let's rearrange the L-C circuit so its components are in series. To do this we convert the matched load resistance and coil (L2 and R2) - which are in parallel - into their series equivalents, L_s and R_s. Hence, we obtain a coil of similar size but a resistor, R_s, of much smaller value. R_s is the series resistance associated with the *loaded Q* of the coil. It's the small resistance that allows the L-C circuit to retain its selectivity. For high Q L-C circuits, R_s will, in most cases, be lower than the antenna resistance. (L1 and C1 are added later; don't worry about them now).

Note, as we stated in the beginning, R_s is smaller than the load or the antenna resistance. Hence, we cannot match the antenna to the load directly; that is, we can't use the main L and C as matching parts and still preserve a high Q. It is necessary to match the antenna and load to the L-C circuit separately.

Finally, our third step, we match the antenna resistance to R_s. This is shown at the left side of (8-1c). Here, we've added a shunt coil and series capacitor at the antenna terminal, L1 and C1 (By lifting C2 from ground and adding L1 and C1 in series). L1 and C1 form an matching network, reducing the antenna resistance to equal R_s. For this match, we can use the formulas outlined in the previous chapter.

Redrawing (c) as (d), by combining C1 and C2, the new circuit takes on a symmetrical form often called the pi-network (due to its shape: π).

HF design example

A design example is shown below using the design procedure just outlined. Let's start by specifying set parameters.

frequency of operation	5.85 Mhz,
headphones	4,000 ohms,
desired bandwidth	50 Khz,
main inductance coil	3.6 μHenry,
resulting coil Q	> 120.

design:

$$w = 2 \cdot \pi \cdot 5.85 \cdot 10^{6} \quad L2 = 3.6 \cdot 10^{-6} \quad C2 = \frac{1}{w^2 \cdot L2}$$

$$C2 = 2.056 \cdot 10^{-10} \quad R_{Load} = 2000 \quad N = 2.6$$

$$R2 = N^2 \cdot R_{Load} \quad R2 = 13.5 \cdot 10^{3} \quad Q2 = \frac{R2}{w \cdot L2}$$

$$Q2 = 102.174 \quad BW = \frac{w}{2 \cdot \pi \cdot Q2} \quad BW = 5.726 \cdot 10^{4}$$

R2 represents the true loading of L2-C2 by the detector and headphones. Our bandwidth, BW, meets our specification, 50 Khz. Now let's transform R2 and L2 into their series equivalent. We will then match R_S to the antenna resistance, R1, by adding L1 and C1.

$$R_{series} = \frac{R2}{Q2^2 + 1} \quad R_{series} = 1.295$$

$$R1 = 50 \quad Q1 = \sqrt{\frac{R1}{R_{series}} - 1} \quad Q1 = 6.133$$

Q1 is the Q of L1, so we can calculate its inductance,

$$L1 = \frac{R1}{Q1 \cdot w} \quad L1 = 2.218 \cdot 10^{-7} \quad XL = L1 \cdot w \quad XL = 8.153$$

Now let's check by going backward,

$$R1 = R_{series}(Q1^2 + 1) \quad R1 = 50$$

Going the other way, checking,

$$R2 = R_{series}(Q2^2 + 1) \quad R2 = 1.352 \cdot 10^4$$

Now, calculate the number of windings necessary to provide 3.6μH of inductance, using the Quick Quaker Oats box:

$$\text{diameter} = 5 \quad \text{length} = 3 \qquad \text{turns} = 5.5$$

$$L2 = \frac{\text{diameter}^2 \cdot \text{turns}^2}{18 \cdot \text{diameter} + 40 \cdot \text{length}}$$

$$L2 = 3.601$$

$$\text{wirelength} = \frac{\pi \cdot \text{diameter} \cdot \text{turns}}{12}$$

$$\text{wirelength} = 7.199 \text{ feet}$$

(8ft of #16 copper wire needed)

Now calculate size needed for coil L1, to match antenna to R_{series}:

$$\text{len} = .3 \quad \text{turns} = 3 \quad \text{dia} = .8 \quad \text{L1 is in microhenry}$$

$$\text{L1} = \frac{\text{dia}^2 \cdot \text{turns}^2}{18 \cdot \text{dia} + 40\text{len}} \qquad L1 = 0.218$$

Now the length for a half-wave dipole to feed the set:

$$\text{dipole} = \frac{492 \cdot (.95)}{5.85} \qquad \text{dipole} = 79.8 \text{ feet}$$

The set was built and works well. A Quick Quaker Oats box, 5 inches in diameter, was used as the coil form, and a 365 μμfd air-variable cap was selected for tuning. A 50 ohm dipole antenna was cut to frequency and used to match the input resistance of the set.

APPENDIX 1

RESISTIVITY AND CONDUCTIVITY OF VARIOUS TYPES OF WIRE

Conductivity, σ, is measured in mhos/meter
Resistivity, ρ, is measured in meter-ohms
All standard constants are measured at 20 °C.

Item	Conductivity 20 degrees C	Conductivity as % of copper	Resistive temp coefficient per degree C
silver	6.1×10^7	106%	.0038
copper	5.7×10^7	100%	.0039
gold	4.1×10^7	70%	.0034
aluminum	3.5×10^7	65%	.0042
brass	1.1×10^7	21-25%	.0020
iron	$.96 \times 10^7$	17%	.0050
tin	$.86 \times 10^7$	15%	.0042

Since resistivity is defined as the reciprocal of conductivity, the resistivity of copper at 20 °C is $1.7 \cdot 10^{-8}$ mhos/meter.

The resistance of any conductor can be computed from the resistivity of the conductor material and its shape. Given the length, cross-sectional area, and resistivity of the material the total (DC) resistance (R) is:

$$R = \rho \cdot \frac{\text{length}}{\text{area}}$$

$$\left[\text{dimensions} = \frac{\text{meter} - (\text{ohms} \cdot \text{meters})}{\text{meters}^2}\right]$$

or

$$\left[\text{dimensions} = \frac{\text{inch} - (\text{ohms} \cdot \text{inches})}{\text{inch}^2}\right]$$

For example, the resistance of a 2 inch diameter, 20 turn coil wound with #20 copper wire is:

$$R = \frac{\left(1.7 \cdot 10^{-8}\right) \cdot \left(\frac{12}{0.305}\right) \cdot 3.14 \cdot 2 \cdot 20}{0.8 \cdot 10^{-3}}$$

$$R = 0.1 \text{ ohm}$$

where:

$1.7 \cdot 10^{-8}$ = the resistivity of the copper

$\frac{12}{0.305}$ = a conversion factor from meters to inches

$3.14 \cdot 2 \cdot 20$ = total wire length in inches (the coil circumference times the number of turns)

$0.8 \cdot 10^{-3}$ = cross-sectional area of #20 wire in square inches

You can calculate coil resistance another way by figuring the length of wire in the coil and comparing it with the ohms/1000 feet listing in the wire table (Appendix 2).

The resistance of metals is affected by temperature changes. The amount of variation of resistance depends on the material but is more or less proportional to temperature. For example, copper is 10% more resistive at 50°C than at 20 °C. Hence the resistance of the coil calculated above would be .13 ohms or 30 percent higher at 100 °C compared to .1 ohm at 20°C.

APPENDIX 2

WIRE TABLE, SOLID COPPER

AWG wire size	mil diameter	turns/inch enamel	tpi DCC	ohms/ 1000 ft
10	101.9	9.1	8.9	1.1
12	80.8	11.3	10.9	1.6
14	64.1	14.0	13.8	2.6
16	50.8	17.3	16.4	4.1
18	40.3	21.2	19.8	6.5
20	32.0	25.8	23.8	10.4
22	25.3	31.3	30.0	16.5
24	20.1	37.6	35.6	26.2
26	15.9	46.1	41.8	41.6
28	12.6	54.6	48.5	66.2
30	10.0	64.1	55.5	105.2

DEFINITIONS:

AWG American wire gauge
DCC double cotton covered
mil .001 inch
tpi turns per inch

BIBLIOGRAPHY

This list represents the ongoing collection of books and articles compiled by the Xtal Set Society and its members. We list all information we have available on each item.

Anderson, Phil. "A Universal Crystal Radio Set." Nuts & Volts, February 1993.

Anwar, Masoud. "A Homemade Radio Powered by Candle." Popular Science, November 1960, pp. 156-158. (*Uses a home-made thermo-couple.*)

Arland, Rich. "A Crystal Set with Volume (by Pete Haas)." Monitoring Times, April 1991, pp. 94.

ARRL Handbook for Radio Amateurs. ARRL: Newington, CT, 1994.

Ballhatchet, A.V. "Wireless Notes-IV." Model Engineer and Electrician, 26 February 1920, a UK pub.

Bates, Will. "Crystal Set for the Boy Builder (il diags)." Popular Mechanics, February 1927, pp. 47:297--8.

Bates, Will. "Inexpensive Crystal Receiver." Popular Mechanics, November 1925, pp. 44:836-8.

Bates, Will. "Radio Set for Fifty Cents." Popular Mechanics, April 1926, pp. 45-473.

Bates, Will. "Selective Crystal Receiver." Popular Mechanics, April 1925, pp.43-680-2.

Beardsley, D.L. "An Electrolytic Wireless Receiver." Scientic American, June 1906.

Bellman, C.H. "Long Distance Crystal Set Receiver." IND Educ. M., March 1925, pp. 26-272-4.

Bliss, Louis D. Theoretical and Practical Electrical Engineering, 1926.

Bouck, Z. "Crystal Receivers are Well Worth While (diags)." Radio Broadcasting, August 1923, pp. 3:319-322.

Boyd, Waldo T. "Build a Modern Day Crystal Set." Popular Electronics, July 1964, p. 53.

Breiner, Allen, W3TI. "The Oatmeal Box Receiver." Worldradio, August 1993, p. 61.

Bucher, Elmer E. Practical Wireless Telegraphy. NY: Wireless Press, 1917.

Bucher, Elmer E. Wireless Experimentor's Manual. NY: Wireless Press, 1922.

Colebrook, F.M. "What is the Best Circuit for Crystal Reception?" The Wireless World and Radio Review, 30 April 1924, pp. 122-124.

Colebrook, F.M. "More About Crystal Reception." The Wireless World and Radio Review, 23 July 1924, pp. 474-477.

Collins, A.F. "Carborundum and Silicon Detectors for Wireless." Scientific American, 16 March 1907.

Crosby, W.F. "From Crystal Set to Superheterodyne (diag)." Literary Digest, 5 August 1922, pp. 74:32-33.

Davidson, Homer. "Super-Charged Crystal Set." Hands-On Electronics, December 1986, pp. 47-51. (*Set and audio-amp combination*).

Davidson, Homer. "Build a Sliding Bar 'Antique' Radio." Hands-On Electronics, December 1988, p. 3942.

Dunlap, Orrin E. Radio's 100 Men of Science. 1944.

Edwards, K.E. Radios that Work for Free. Grants Pass, Oregon: Hope and Allen Publishing, 1977.

Escoffier, Jim. "Broadcast Radio Uses Home-Made Components." RF Design, June 1993, p. 84.

Fitch, Clyde. "Oscillating Crystals." The Experimenter, March 1925, p. 298.

Ghirardi, Alfred. Radio Physics Course, 1932.

Graf, Calvin R. Exploring Light, Radio and Sound Energy with Projects. Tab Books.

Green, Charles. All About Crystal Sets. California: All About Books, 1984.

Haas, Peter. "Powerful Crystal Set." 73 Magazine, April 1989.

Harvie, G.A. "Construction of a Crystal Detector Receiving Set." IND ARTS M, August 1923, pp. 12:316-17.

Henney, K. "Good Crystal Set for the Beginner (il diag.)." Radio Broadcasting, June 1928, pp. 13:97-8.

Hertzberg, Robert. "Make This MIDGET RADIO Set." Mechanix Illustrated, March 1949, pp. 100-140.

Hirsch, Harry. "Pill Box RADIO." Mechanix Illustrated, January 1947, pp. 118-119.

Johnson, Henry. "A Short-Wave Crystal Tuner." Old Timer's Bulletin, AWA, August 1992.

Judd, Phillippe. "Radio Outfit In a Headset." The Experimenter, October 1925. (*The circuit is inside the one headphone and the coil mounts on your head!*).

Lewis, Tom. Empire of the Air. Harper Collins, 1991.

Lyon, Terry. "How To Build 'Free-Power' Radios." Electronic Experimenter's Handbook, 1976 Edition, pp. 60-61. (*Describes three one-transistor, battery-less receivers*).

McQuay, Jordan. "Crystal Detectors." Radio-Craft, July 1948.

Moody, J.H. "A Practical Pocket Crystal Set." Model Engineer and Electrician. April 1924, a UK pub.

Mount, H.A. "Crystals that Speak." Scientific American, 5 June 1920.

Newlands, R.G. "The Coherer Revisited - Some Experiments." Break-In, Australia, September 1990.

Nilson, Arthur R. Practical Radio Communications. McGraw Hill Book Company, 1943.

Obrian, Pat. "Old-Time Crystal Radio." Radio Electronics, October 1986, pp. 54-55,101. (*Nice spider-web coil plan*).

Osberne, J.M. G3HMO. "Crystal Receiver with Self-Powered Transistor AMP." The Short Wave Magazine, July 1956.

Patzer, William. "Operation Crystal." GE-Ham News, March 1955.

Payor, Steve. "Build a Matchbox Crystal Radio." Popular Electronics, June 1989.

Pierce, George W. Principles of Wireless Telegraphy, McGraw Hill, 1910.

Pickard, Greenleaf W. "In Justice of the Crystal Set." Popular Science Monthly, September 1922.

Pickard, Greenleaf W. "How I Invented the Crystal Detector." Electrical Experimenter, 1919.

Rakes, Charles. "Crystal Diode Detectors." Hands-on Electronics, December 1988, pp. 82-83,99.

Riley, P.M. "Regenerative Radio Reception (diag)." Radio Broadcasting, November 1922, pp. 2:58-62.

Robbins, Lawrence. "Make the Parts for These Crystal Sets." Popular Mechanics, January 1944, pp. 142-143. (Includes some detail on a rotor coil, variometer).

Rubens, N.J. "Selective, Fixed Detector Crystal Set." Science.

Schoo, Daniel. "Restoring Galena Crystal Detectors." Antique Radio Classified, November 1991.

Sievers, Maurice L. Crystal Clear.

Smith, Keith G3JIX. "Build a Crystal Set." D-i-Y Radio (England), September 1993.

Stanley, Rupert. Text Book on Wireless Telegraphy. Longmans, Green and Co., 1916.

Strand, Arnold. "Cigar Box Radio." Mechanix Illustrated, April 1946, pp. 130-131.

Stratton, S.W. Construction and Operation of a Simple Radio. Washington DC: Circular 120 Bureau Standards, 24 April 1922.

Stratton, S.W. Construction and Operation of Two-Circuit Radio. Washington DC: Circular 121 Bureau Standards, 17 July 1922.

Tester, Ross. "Let's Talk About Crystal Sets - Part I." Elementary Electronics, October 1973.

Tester, Ross. "Let's Talk About Crystal Sets - Part II." Elementary Electronics, November 1973, pp. 85-88.

Tobin, Frank. "The Last Word in Crystal Sets." Popular Science, February 1947, pp. 190-193. (*Four sets featured*).

Trauffer, Art. "Learning New Tricks from an Ancient Rig." Electronics Hobbyist, Fall-Winter 1971, pp. 27-33.

Trauffer, Art. "Oatmeal Box Crystal Radio." Elementary Electronics, March 1975.

Trauffer, Art. "Push-Pull Crystal Receiver." Elementary Electronics.

"A Sensational Radio Invention." Literary Digest, 20 September 1924, pp. 20:28-29. (*talks about the crystaldyne, oscillating crystals*).

"Announcing Operation Crystal." G-E Ham News, January 1955.

"Back to the Crystal Set." Literary Digest, 4 November 1922.

"Build a Crystal Set, The Original Solid-State Radio." Popular Mechanics, January 1977.

"Crystal Sets go on For Ever." Wireless Weekly, 26 June 1931.

"Construction of a Crystal Detector Receiving Set." IND ARTS M, January 1923, pp.12-316.

"Homemade Receiving Set." Literary Digest, 8 July 1922, pp. 74-25.

"Loop Arials for Broadcast Reception." Radio Broadcasting, November 1922.

"Powerful Crystal Radio Brings in Distant Stations." Modern Mechanix, January, 1936, p. 36.

"Seven Crystal Sets for Beginners." Popular Mechanics, July, Year?, pp. 138-178.

"Simplest Radio Receiver (il diag)." Literary Digest, 22 April 1922, pp. 73:27-8.

"The Ten Best Crystal Circuits." Popular Hobbies, January 1931, pp 6-7,60.

"Two Modern Crystal Sets." Popular Mechanics, February 1943, p. 156.

"What Causes Fading?" Radio Broadcasting, November 1923.

"Where Crystal Sets Do the Trick." Popular Science, June 1932, pp. 120-167.

"Wireless Receivers, Simple Radio Receiving Sets." Scientific American, July 1921, pp. 4-79.

THE XTAL SET SOCIETY

The Xtal Set Society ***Newsletter***, bi-monthly, one year subscription. Postage is included.	$ 9.95

International subscriptions please remit US$16.00, Canadians please remit US$11.00.

Volume I of the Society Newsletter, six issues, ending May, 1992.	$ 9.95
Volume II of the Society Newsletter, six issues, ending May, 1993.	$ 9.95
Volume IV of the Society Newsletter, six issues, ending November 1995.	$ 9.95
Volume V of the Society Newsletter, six issues, ending November 1996.	$ 9.95

Other titles available:

Radio that Work for Free	$ 9.95
All About Crystal Sets	$ 9.95
Crystal Clear, Volume I	$29.95
Crystal Clear, Volume II	$29.95

Shipping and handling on all book orders	$ 2.50

International orders $4.50 shipping. Missouri residents please add 5.975% sales tax.

The Xtal Set Society, P.O. Box 3026
St. Louis, MO 63130, (314) 725-1172
VISA/MC accepted

ABOUT THE AUTHOR

Phil Anderson became interested in radio at the age of 13. He started out building and experimenting with Heathkits and soon after had his amateur radio license. His curiosity and desire to understand the magic of radio has always driven him to do things other people think are a little crazy. As a teenager he woke up his mother in the middle of the night by stringing antennas on the roof. When his older brother brought a date home, Phil would annoyingly tune his radio to make his brother's radio "howl". His mother always wondered what he was doing in his room, especially the time he yelped after touching his nose to the anode of a 2E26. After all these years he is still interested in radio and electronics. He loves the beauty of math and mechanisms that work but cannot be seen.

Phil was born in Tracy Minnesota in 1941. He received his Doctor of Engineering degree from the University of Kansas in 1970. In 1971 he co-founded Kantronics where he now manufacturers radio modems. Phil and his wife Pat live in Lawrence, Kansas.

NOTES: